OTHER
SUNS.
OTHER
WORLDS?

OTHER SUNS, OTHER WORLDS?

DENNIS L. MAMMANA

AND

DONALD W. MCCARTHY, JR.

ST. MARTIN'S PRESS ✹ NEW YORK

Design by Pei Koay

Library of Congress Cataloging-in-Publication
Data

Mammana, Dennis.
    Other suns. other worlds? / by Dennis L.
Mammana and Donald W. McCarthy, Jr.—1st ed.
        p.   cm.
    ISBN 0-312-14021-5
    1. Solar system. 2. Planetology. I. Mc-
Carthy, Donald W., Jr.   II. Title.
QB501.M34 1996
523.2—dc20   95-40391
                                         CIP

First Edition: May 1996

10 9 8 7 6 5 4 3 2 1

To Diane,

whose understanding during this long,

difficult project exceeded all worldly expectations.

From one writer to another:

Thank you!

—D.L.M.

To Mom & Dad,

whose vast curiosity, encouragement,

and enthusiasm have shaped my

life and enabled me to pursue

exploration

—D.W.M.

ACKNOWLEDGMENTS

During the course of research, writing, and publication of any book, there are many people who contribute to its success.

For their selfless sharing of ideas and data on the search for extrasolar planetary systems and related topics, the authors wish to thank Roger Angel, Dana Backman, David Black, Robert Brown, Vera Buescher, Bruce Campbell, William Cochran, Michael Crowe, Frank Drake, George Gatewood, Fred Gillett, Robert Harrington, Wes Huntress, Mike Kaplan, Eugene Levy, Sarah Lee Lippincott, Frank Low, Jonathan Lunine, Robert McMillan, George Rieke, Seth Shostak, Bradford Smith, Lori Stiles, Jill Tarter, Rich Terrile, Gordon Walker, Ewen Whitaker, Tom Worthen, and Ben Zuckerman.

Special thanks must go to our agent, Julie Castiglia, for her persistent encouragement and help in negotiating the seemingly endless hurdles we faced, and to our editor, Keith Kahla, for his patience and expert guidance in making this project a reality.

CONTENTS

OTHER SUNS.
OTHER WORLDS?

INTRODUCTION

Anyone who has ever gazed into the nighttime sky has undoubtedly been struck by the majesty of the starry heavens. Indeed, it is a rare person who does not gasp in amazement at the number of stars visible on a clear, dark night, and does not wonder at the possibility of other beings gazing out into their own skies in similar wonder. But the sky visible to the naked eye is but a minute portion of a universe far more vast than humans can imagine.

In many ways, each star is a sun like that which lights the Earth. Each is a thermonuclear generator, converting hydrogen to helium in its core and producing staggering amounts of energy that radiate outward in the form of light and heat. In fact, the sun—which, by generating weather and photosynthesis makes it possible for life to survive on the Earth—is very much a *normal* star. And thousands like it are scattered about space. The nearest of these, believed today to be Proxima Centauri, lies at a staggering distance of 41 trillion kilometers from Earth—so far that a beam of light traveling at a speed of nearly 300,000 kilometers per second requires 4.3 years to make the journey—a distance of 4.3 "light-years."

Beyond this "solar neighborhood" lie billions of other stars, many linked by gravity into binary systems—some into clusters of hundreds or thousands. Between the stars, space is far from empty: it is permeated by expansive and colorful clouds of gas and dust, some of which reflect the light of nearby stars, some which glow brightly on their own. Still others are so thick that they block the light of more distant stars and appear only in silhouette.

Four hundred billion stars, star clusters, and interstellar clouds make up the spiral structure that astronomers call the Milky Way galaxy. It spans a distance of at least 600,000 trillion miles— 100,000 light-years—from side to side, yet it is only 4,000 light-years thick near its edge. The sun and its planetary family reside on the inner edge of one of the galaxy's colossal spiral arms, about two-thirds of the way out from the galactic center. From this vantage point, the blended light of all those stars makes the galactic disk appear as a hazy, mottled cloud of light stretching across the nighttime sky of Earth. From the outside, the Milky Way would appear as a gigantic pinwheel with a bulge at its center, and with the sun and its planetary family—a mere speck against the vastness of the galaxy—totally lost from view.

As immense as the Milky Way is, it is but one of hundreds of millions of similar structures scattered throughout the sky—each a galaxy in its own right. One of the nearest is known as the Great Galaxy in Andromeda, 2 million light-years away. It appears on a dark November night as a hazy smudge, the combined light of hundreds of billions of stars—each a possible home to a planetary system.

Just as stars tend to form in clusters so, too, do galaxies. The Milky Way and the Andromeda galaxy are but two members of a galactic family called the Local Group. Though this grouping stretches some 2.5 million light-years from end to end, astronomers know it as a "dwarf" cluster that lies on the outskirts of an even larger grouping: the Local Supercluster. And beyond lie even more clusters and superclusters as far as the largest telescopes can see—some as distant as 17 billion light-years.

With such an immense cosmos lying before us on a clear dark night, who among us can gaze outward and not wonder how many planetary systems must exist among the stars of our home star city? And how many of these might be home to life—some, perhaps, similar to that of Earth; some, perhaps, quite different?

Lofty questions, yes, but it is not just the astronomers and cosmic number crunchers who concern themselves with such. Gallup Polls of the general public in recent years indicate that the belief in the existence of extraterrestrial life is not only widespread, but growing rapidly. When asked in 1966 if they believe that "people somewhat like ourselves exist on other planets," 34 percent of those polled said yes; seven years later, 46 percent answered affirmatively. By 1978, the positive vote had grown to 51 percent.

Other surveys have shown even higher percentages. For example, in 1977 *Scholastic Magazines* conducted a nationwide survey of 27,000 youngsters; 76 percent believed that life on Earth is not unique. A 1981 *Glamour* magazine survey showed that 85 percent of its 2 million readers believed that other worlds exist and are home to intelligent life. An ABC Television poll in 1982 reported that 32,233 of 35,758 telephone callers (90 percent) said they believe that extraterrestrial life exists. A 1985 study of 883 "national leaders" showed startling numbers: 90 percent of science policy leaders, 89 percent of environmental organization leaders, and 88 percent of religious leaders said they believe there is life elsewhere in the universe. And in a nationwide CNN poll taken in February of 1990, 85 percent of those polled expressed similar beliefs.

In fact, the concept that other worlds exist among the stars, and that life may exist on them, has become such an accepted part of modern culture that it seems difficult for most people to believe otherwise. "Extraterrestrial life is a very pliable concept," explains Dr. Michael J. Crowe, a historian at the University of Notre Dame who has studied this phenomenon for years. "You can adjust it to most any philosophy you want, and you can get it to do a lot of different forms of work for you. There's not just one reason why people believe in extraterrestrials either. If you're a pessimist or an optimist, an idealist or a realist, a materialist, a theist or an atheist, you can adjust extraterrestrial life ideas to fit. And the concept can give it a kind of 'cosmic scope' and make it appear to fit your personal philosophy and the latest results of science."

Now, while gazing into the starry night sky and pondering the existence of other Earths and other beings seems like a fascinating pastime to many, one might debate its practical purposes. After all, even if there are other worlds among the stars—populated or not—we are not likely to visit them anytime in the near future. And the existence of other worlds will not pay our mortgages, feed our children, or settle our worldly disputes. So why should anyone even care?

We care because we're human and, as such, are explorers. It is, after all, the exploration of our cosmic neighborhood with manned and robot spacecraft that has altered the way we look at planet Earth. When humans first left the bounds of our planet in the 1960s, they saw the Earth for the first time with no political or religious boundaries, no ethnic or racial differences—indeed, not even a bit of direct evidence of the existence of life. And they returned to us photographs and firsthand accounts of the rocky and watery planet suspended in the darkness—a fragile world whose resources were limited and must be shared by all its creatures.

Because we were curious enough to explore and to ask questions that some believed were best left unasked—a paradigm began to change. And the Earth and its people would never be the same again. We now stand on the verge of another such paradigm shift as astronomers look at the stars not as sites of thermonuclear fusion, but as possible homes to planets and planetary systems. And we are again beginning to think of our Earth in a new light—not as a special and unique place in the universe, but as one of many and varied worlds that may have been born out of similar processes. And we are beginning to view the beings with which we share our planet not as blacks and whites, Arabs and Jews, rich and poor, but as *people of planet Earth*.

The question of our world's uniqueness is not just a fascinating puzzle to be pondered by pompous eggheads in ivory-tower academia. It is one whose answer—whether positive or negative—will touch each and every one of us in some way.

Today, the search for other worlds has reached a fever pitch in some circles—and astronomers are running a veritable race to be the first to make a discovery. And why not? The debate over the existence of other worlds and other life had raged long and hard for centuries. Ours is the first generation with the technology to answer the questions once and for all.

But the search is tremendously difficult at best. The nearest star where planets might conceivably exist is Proxima Centauri, at a distance of 4.3 light-years from Earth, with others of the Milky Way galaxy extending 100,000 light-years away. At these distances, even immense stars appear tiny, and planets—only a fraction of the size of their parent stars—are exceedingly difficult to see. But more difficult than spotting the disk of an extrasolar planet is trying to see its reflected light over the glare of its parent star. At best, this requires huge telescopes, perfect atmospheric conditions, sophisticated electronic detectors, and a considerable amount of luck. Despite the problems inherent in trying to find such bodies, and ultimately, other beings, most astronomers believe it is possible. And they have set out to do just that: find worlds in orbit around distant stars.

This is the story of their search.

1

THE DREAM BEGINS

". . . there are infinite worlds both like and unlike this world of ours. For the atoms being infinite in number . . . are borne far out in space. For those atoms . . . have not been used up either on one world or on a limited number of worlds, nor on all the worlds which are alike, or on all those which are different from these. So that there nowhere exists an obstacle to the infinite number of worlds. . . . we must believe that in all worlds there are living creatures and plants and other things we see in this world . . ."

—EPICURUS (341–270 B.C.)
LETTER TO HERODOTUS

In his *Letter to Herodotus* more than two millennia ago, the famous Greek thinker Epicurus expressed his view that our familiar world was not the only one that existed. It shouldn't surprise anyone that such a "modern" idea existed so long ago. The Greeks, after all, were like many other ancient civilizations in that they were constant watchers of the sky.

But the Greek philosophers were unique in one sense. They were not constrained by a religion that tied their interpretations of nature and the heavens to the whims of capricious gods. They did not believe that nature was controlled by gods and, therefore, was outside the realm of human understanding. Instead, they believed that the universe functioned according to physical laws that all could be described by logic and mathematics. Once these laws were understood, the workings of the universe would be secrets no longer.

One of the cornerstones of their cosmology was that the universe was infinite—that it existed forever in both space and time. In such an infinite universe, the Greeks believed, the Earth could hardly be the sole dwelling place of life. In fact, this idea was born long before Epicurus wrote his now-famous words. It was

Thales of Miletus, perhaps the first true astronomer in history, who taught in the sixth century B.C. that both the stars and the Earth were composed of the same materials. And his pupil, Anaximander, extrapolated further that if the universe is infinite and the makeup of all its parts is identical, then the number of worlds in space must also be infinite, with some in the throes of birth and death at all times.

At first glance, it might seem that these philosophers were millennia ahead of their time, pondering and teaching the existence of other planets in orbit around distant stars. But we are of different times and of different perspectives, and must always be careful not to impose our modern biases on their ideas. To the ancients, the expression "worlds" meant something completely different than it does today. The "world" consisted of the land on which they lived, the air they breathed, the sky upon which the sun, moon, and planets revolved on crystalline spheres, and, beyond, the vault of the stars. Other "worlds" consisted of similar systems, each with its own earth, air, and starry heavens.

"In Greek and Roman times, other 'worlds' meant other systems invisible to us," explains historian Michael J. Crowe of the University of Notre Dame. "They weren't identified by planets or stars. Instead, each would be a whole system like ours—an Earth, a sun and planets going around it, and a starry ball where all the stars are just points on a huge vault like a planetarium roof. There would be a number of systems like that which would have an 'Earth' at its center and all those various celestial bodies going around it. And when people referred to the plurality of worlds, they really meant the plurality of *inhabited* worlds in nearly every case."

The Greeks believed that an infinite universe would naturally contain an infinite number of such worlds. Each would be inhabited by intelligent beings, for if they weren't, these worlds would have been considered a tremendous waste of the Creator's time and talents. That this infinity of "worlds" existed came not from observation, but from analogy. Metrodorus of Chios, a contemporary of Epicurus, presented his analogy to explain the existence of other worlds: "To consider the Earth the only populated world in infinite space," he wrote, "is as absurd as to assert that in an entire field sown with millet only one grain will grow." From analogy, the ancient Greeks developed universal theories that held for many centuries, among them, that this world was only one of many inhabited worlds throughout the cosmos.

One of the greatest proponents of Epicurean philosophy came about 350 years later: the Roman philosopher Titus Lucretius Carus, generally referred to as Lucretius. Lucretius took a far more sophisticated view of the place of the world in the cosmos. He maintained that all matter consists of atoms which, unchanging themselves, can rearrange into different forms throughout the infinite universe and give rise to an abundance of worlds and a diversity of life. In his famous poem *De Rerum Natura*, Lucretius writes:

> Granted, then, that empty space extends without limit in every direction and that seeds innumerable are rushing on countless courses through an unfathomable universe . . . , it is in the highest degree unlikely that this earth and sky is the only one to have been created and that all those particles are accomplishing nothing. This follows from the fact that our world has been made by the spontaneous and casual collision and the multifarious, accidental, random and purposeless congregation and coalescence of atoms whose suddenly formed combinations could serve [to produce] . . . earth and sea and sky and the races of living creatures.

With this far more advanced view, Lucretius laid a foundation upon which modern perspectives are based. But not all philosophers of his time agreed with Lucretius. Many assumed the existence of only one universe that was centered around Earth. One such nonbeliever was Aristotle, whose works encompassed varied subjects including philosophy, history, politics, ethics, poetry, drama, biology, and astronomy.

In his *On the Heavens,* Aristotle accomplished what no other philosopher had ever done: he melded the ideas of his predecessors into one complete model of the universe. Aristotle based his concept of the natural system primarily on the inherent tendencies of matter. He believed that the universe was composed of four elements—earth, water, air, and fire—and that each had a natural place. Earth and water were heaviest and naturally moved downward, while the lighter elements, air and fire, always moved upward.

In describing the "world," Aristotle reasoned that the Earth must be a sphere, for if all material fell downward, a sphere is the only shape it could produce. Because of the natural tendency of heavy elements to fall downward, Aristotle reasoned, the Earth must lie at the center of universe, surrounded by an ocean of water, a sphere of air, and a sphere of fire. And, since the Earth was incredibly heavy, it could not possibly move and therefore must be stationary. Revolving about this immovable Earth each day were seven crystalline spheres that carried with them the sun, moon, and five planets. Surrounding *them* was a sphere carrying the fixed stars. This, Aristotle argued, was the "world."

Beyond, Aristotle proposed the most perfect of all spheres— the *Primum Mobile*—the First Mover. It carried no bodies, but was instead the master gear that set in motion all the spheres that made this "world." Whether other worlds existed beyond, Aristotle had no doubts. There could be no others, for if there were, they, too, would be composed of earth, water, air, and fire. If part of the earth, for example, moved downward toward *another* world, it must move *upward* relative to ours—a severe contradiction that must mean that ours was the only world possible. And if that weren't convincing enough, Aristotle called upon religion to further bolster his case. He argued that if more than one world existed, there must be more than one *Primum Mobile*. And that was something he could not accept.

By the fourth century A.D., two strongly opposing schools of thought had developed throughout Europe. One, based on the Epicurean and Lucretian philosophies, held that other worlds and other forms of life were not only possible but *likely* to exist throughout the universe. The other, originated by Aristotle, was based upon the belief that this world is the center of all that is, and that no other worlds or life could possibly exist.

As rational and logical as the Epicurean philosophy was, it was Aristotle's eloquent depiction of the dichotomy between the perfection of heaven and the imperfection of Earth that captured the imagination of the Catholic Church and with it the minds of millions throughout Western Europe. During this time, few people dared challenge his wisdom and that of the Church. Certainly debates erupted from time to time, but most rejected outright the notion that other worlds existed. Some even asserted that an omnipotent God *could*, if He wanted to, create multiple worlds, though most everyone knew He didn't do so.

With the power base of the Church expanding rapidly, Europe began to slip silently into a twelve-hundred-year coma during which learning and discovery gave way to faith and blind acceptance. The Dark Ages had fallen.

THEN THERE WAS LIGHT . . .

Then, in the sixteenth century, a young Polish canon of the Catholic Church named Nicolaus Copernicus put forth a mathematical idea so revolutionary that it rocked the very foundations of human consciousness. The Earth, he wrote, was not the center of the universe as everyone had always believed, but was, instead, merely *one* of the planets orbiting the *sun*.

In 1530, Copernicus completed his book entitled *De Revolutionibus Orbium Coelestium (On the Revolutions of the Celestial Orbs)*, and word of his radical theories spread throughout Europe. Copernicus, however, knew that to contradict the Church and Aristotle was an unforgivable sin and was not confident enough to publish the book. Perhaps his reluctance came from attacks he received from the likes of Martin Luther, who wrote: "Mention has been made of some new astrologer, who wants to teach that the Earth moves around, not the firmament or heavens, the sun and moon . . . This fool seeks to overturn the whole art of astronomy. But as the Holy Scriptures show, Jehovah ordered the sun, not the Earth, to stand still."

Thirteen years later, at the determined insistence of a young professor named Georg Joachim Von Lauchen, more commonly known as Rhæticus, the aging astronomer relented and published the book. But Copernicus never had a chance to read the final product, for only months before it was released he suffered a stroke that left him weak and bedridden. Legend tells that when the first copy rolled off the press on May 24, 1543, and was rushed to his bedside, Copernicus looked up and weakly touched its cover. A few hours later, he died. Perhaps it's just as well for had he opened the book, he would have been furious. The publisher, in trying to soften the impact of the book, had written an anonymous disclaimer, describing the work as merely a means of performing more accurate astronomical calculations, and not a true expression of reality.

Even with the disclaimer, the book provoked the wrath of the Catholic Church. In it Copernicus had undermined the authority of the Holy Bible by removing the Earth from its time-honored position at the center of the universe, and single-handedly set the world in motion. In 1616, the Church placed the work on its list of forbidden books, a dubious honor that wasn't lifted for nearly two centuries.

With his simple yet controversial ideas, Copernicus set the world in motion. Perhaps even more importantly, he set the minds of European scholars in motion. If Copernicus's ideas were true, many thought—if the Earth were, indeed, just one of several planets orbiting the sun—then those other planets may be similar to ours. His ideas began to give legitimacy to the Epicurean notion that other worlds might exist beyond. But now, the word "world" took on an entirely new definition. It came to mean "planet"—a place perhaps much like Earth. The stars, it seemed, might be suns, orbited by such worlds—each of which might be home to life. And, over the years, scholars began to speculate once again about the possibilities—this time in a very new and different way.

One of those who challenged the wisdom of the ages was the sixteenth-century Italian monk Giordano Bruno. In his *De l'Infinito Universo e Mondi (On the Infinite Universe and Worlds)*, Bruno wrote a debate between two fictional philosophers named Burchio and Fracastorio, in which he soundly rejected the natural philosophy of Aristotle that the Earth was the center of the universe, and cleverly expounded his own ideas about the plurality of worlds:

> . . . we know that there is an infinite field, a containing space which does embrace and interpenetrate the whole. In it is an infinity of bodies similar to our own. No one of these more than another is in the centre of the universe, for the universe is infinite and therefore without centre or limit, . . . there are certain determined definite centres, namely the suns, fiery bodies around which revolve all planets, earths and waters, even as we see the seven wandering planets take their course around our sun . . . Thus there is not merely one world, one earth, one sun, but as many worlds as we see bright lights around us, which are neither more nor less in one heaven, one space, one containing sphere than is this our world in one containing universe, one space or one heaven.

For daring to challenge the authority of the Church and the word of Aristotle with such "heretical" views, Bruno was imprisoned for seven years, the first two without even a cloak or a pillow. Still, Bruno remained convinced that his ideas were correct. Finally, after refusing to renounce his views, Bruno was tried by a tribunal of the Inquisition, excommunicated, and burned at the stake in Rome on February 17, 1600.

Unfortunately, Bruno had no scientific evidence to support

his beliefs. Had he lived a bit longer, his life might have been spared, for barely a few years after his death, word of a remarkable new invention—the telescope—came from Holland. Bruno's countryman Galileo Galilei heard of this new instrument, built one, and aimed it toward the heavens.

THROUGH THE LOOKING GLASS

The importance of the telescope to the field of astronomy in general, and the question of the plurality of worlds in particular, cannot be overestimated. Until the early seventeenth century, sky watchers could only gaze upward with their eyes and use some rudimentary tools to measure positions and brightnesses of the celestial objects. Now, suddenly, a new tool was available, one that opened a new window on the universe. And, while he was not the first to build a telescope or even aim it at the sky, Galileo did recognize the astronomical significance of the telescope and built several for systematic research of the heavens.

In his first outing with his new instrument, Galileo found that the moon was peppered with Earth-like features: craters, rills, and valleys. There were towering mountains that he measured to be as high as 4 miles above the lunar surface. In what must have been an astonishing moment of discovery, Galileo realized that the moon was not the smooth, perfect sphere that had been described by the ancient philosophers. It appeared, instead, as a world similar to Earth itself. But how similar, he must have wondered. Did it have water and air? Were there people, vegetation, and animals populating its surface? Or was it a silent, dead world unlike anything known here on Earth?

On January 7, 1610, Galileo aimed his telescope toward Jupiter and found that it was a world as well, appearing as a tiny disk among the pinpoint stars. Nearby, Galileo noticed several bright points of light—two to Jupiter's east and one to its west, sketched their positions, and excitedly went about his observing. The following night, he looked again but now the three "stars" all appeared to the planet's west. The following night it was cloudy, but by the tenth of the month, the skies had cleared and Galileo was at work again. This time, only two "stars" appeared next to Jupiter, and both were to its east. By now, Galileo must have realized he was on to something unusual since if Jupiter had moved past these stars in its orbit, or was somehow swinging like a pendulum relative to them, it was not behaving as mathematics had predicted.

Night after night, Galileo observed Jupiter and its companion "stars." Soon, a fourth had appeared and it, too, seemed to move relative to Jupiter. It wasn't long before Galileo had theorized that the "stars" that had so intrigued him weren't stars at all, but moons orbiting the giant planet from night to night, and changing their positions in the sky. But if this were true, Galileo reasoned, then the Earth could not be the center of the universe as had long been believed, but that it was the sun about which all revolved. And if worlds could orbit other worlds, perhaps they could orbit other suns as well.

Galileo also observed the planet Venus and found that it appeared quite different from Jupiter. Not only did it not have any moons in orbit around it, but it seemed to change its size and shape as it moved about the sky, often appearing like the Earth's moon. At times, he saw it as a large, thin crescent. Over several weeks, he watched as it shrunk in size until it displayed a "quarter" phase. And just before disappearing into the glare of the sun weeks later, it appeared as a tiny, full disk. Galileo concluded that he could see the phases of Venus only if it revolved around the sun and not the Earth.

From all the observational evidence at hand, Galileo could only conclude that the Earth was one of many worlds in orbit around the Sun. Copernicus, it seemed, was right after all. Once the sun was placed at the center of the planetary system, the stars became suns, which opened the possibility that they, too, might have planetary systems in orbit around them.

Just as his predecessors, Galileo knew that these discoveries contradicted the wisdom of the ancient philosophers, not to mention the teachings of the Catholic Church. While Galileo was a good Catholic and wished no harm to come to his Church or to its teachings, he was also a first-rate scientist, and he knew the facts when he saw them. The Earth was merely one of the planets, and it orbited the central and motionless sun; not the other way around. In his attempt to convince Church officials of the true workings of the universe, Galileo showed them his discoveries through the telescope and explained his ideas in detail. Despite his efforts, Galileo landed himself in serious trouble with authorities. For his "crimes" of teaching that the sun and not the Earth was the center of the universe, Galileo was placed under house arrest, where he died several years later, a tired, broken old man.

Nevertheless, Galileo's work and ideas had elevated astronomy to a new plateau, one in which a powerful new tool could be used to examine the universe in greater detail. Astronomers around the world had begun to construct bigger and better telescopes and were soon discovering and cataloging an amazing array of objects and phenomena around the sky. They found that stars not only existed as single bodies, but also appeared within groups from two to thousands. They learned that the sky was littered with nebulous clouds, many of which had no distinct shape whatsoever, but some of which appeared in spiral or elongated patterns. They found that not only did Jupiter have moons in orbit about it, but so did Saturn, along with its brilliant, glorious rings. Astronomers also began regular searches for the unpredictable comets that occasionally appeared in the sky.

GETTING THE WORD OUT

The seventeenth century was, without question, the greatest period of astronomical advances that had ever been experienced. The religious dogma of a central and motionless Earth that had held European minds hostage for more than a millennium was now being overthrown. Few astronomers still doubted that the Earth was one of the planets, and that all orbited a central, motionless sun. The idea that the sun was a star, and that each nighttime star could be a distant home to its own unique planetary system began to capture the imagination like never before. Gradually, the "plurality of worlds" became transformed from a belief of a few to one of virtual certainty that was published in scientific textbooks, taught in the classroom, and preached from the pulpit.

One of the greatest contributors to this change was Bernard le Bovier de Fontenelle, who, in 1686, published his immensely popular book *Entretiens sur la Pluralité des Mondes (Conversations on the Plurality of the Worlds)*. Perhaps the first truly "popular" science book, *Entretiens* combined Fontenelle's elegant prose with the scientific knowledge of the day to delight its readers and to inspire them with the idea that other worlds orbiting the sun are similar to the Earth, and that other stars are actually suns orbited by other planets. It presented five, and eventually six, dialogues between a fictitious philosopher and a charming marquise:

> The moon, says I, is inhabited, because she is like the earth; and the other planets are inhabited, because they are like the moon; I find the fixed stars resemble our sun; therefore I attribute to them what is proper to him.
>
> But, says the lady, if you build upon this resemblance, or likeness, which is between our sun and the fixed stars, then, to the people of another great vortex, our sun must appear no larger than a small fixed star, and can be seen only when it is night with them. Without doubt, madam, says I, it must be so: our sun is much nearer to us, than the suns of other vortexes, and therefore its light makes a much greater impression on our eyes than theirs do: we see nothing but the light of our own sun; and when we see him, it darkens and hinders us from seeing any other; but in another great vortex, there is another sun, which rules and governs; and, in his turn, extinguishes the light of our sun, which is never seen there but in the night, with the rest of the other suns, that is, the fixed stars; with them our sun

is suspended in the great arched roof of heaven, where it makes a part of some constellation: the planets which turn round about it (our earth for example), as they are not seen at so vast a distance, so nobody will so much as dream of them.

As wonderfully elegant and educational as Fontenelle's story was, the Catholic Church pronounced it dangerous. This time, however, the public wasn't believing it. They purchased the book in record numbers, and within two years, *Entretiens* was available in three languages, and eventually in a dozen.

While Fontenelle's book was inspiring, astronomers needed a more technical development of the idea. In 1698, a work by Dutch mathematician and physicist Christiaan Huygens was published three years after his death. *Cosmotheoros* first appeared in Latin and then in English, as *Celestial Worlds Discover'd*. In it, Huygens not only reiterated speculation about the planets and their habitability presented by the greatest thinkers in history, but he advanced his own ideas as well. What made his work unique was that he separated, for the first time, conjecture from scientific fact and skillfully assessed their probabilities.

In his book, Huygens described the moon as a waterless and lifeless world. He explained that the spots found on Jupiter were nothing more than clouds, and that Venus was cloaked by a cloudy atmosphere. Most of the evidence that Huygens cited suggested that life on other planets in this solar system was improbable but that elsewhere in the universe, anything was possible. He wrote that the qualities of Earth's planetary neighbors,

we must likewise grant to all those planets that surround that prodigious number of suns. They must have their plants and animals, nay and their rational creatures too, and those as great admirers, and as diligent observers of the heavens as ourselves . . .

Huygens anticipated one severe objection to these ideas: If planets do orbit other stars, why can't astronomers see them? Certainly the telescope was making a mockery of distances, revealing in detail hitherto invisible celestial objects. If extrasolar planets existed, why hadn't anyone found them? To answer this legitimate and profound question, Huygens used mathematics to determine the visibility of planets in orbit around distant stars. He began by estimating how far the sun would have to be removed to appear as bright as the wintertime star Sirius. The answer was an astonishing "trillions of kilometers." From this he reasoned that any planets orbiting such a distant star would appear much too tiny and faint to be visible from Earth, even with the most powerful telescopes of the late seventeenth century.

During the first four decades of the following century, it was not only the science-minded who were concerned with "pluralism." For example, the English poet Alexander Pope believed that, throughout the vast universe, there existed a smooth gradation in material size from the small to the large, as well as in the senses and mental faculties of all living creatures. In his famous *Essay on Man,* he expressed his opinion that the proper study of human existence must include consideration of other worlds and their inhabitants.

> He, who through vast immensity can pierce,
> See worlds on worlds compose one universe,
> Observe how system into system runs,
> What other planets circle other suns,
> What vary'd Being peoples every star,
> May tell why Heav'n has made us as we are.

And Richard Blackmore, in his long poem entitled *The Creation*, wrote of other worlds:

> Yet in this mighty system, which contains
> So many worlds, such vast etherial plains,

But one of thousands, which compose the whole,
Perhaps as glorious, and of worlds as full.
All these illustrious worlds, and many more,
Which by the tube astronomers explore;
And millions which the glas can n'er descry,
Lost in the wilds of vast immensity;
Are suns, are centres, whose superior sway
Planets of various magnitude obey.

As widespread as the idea was becoming, however, some felt that a belief in pluralism might somehow conflict with Christianity while others were beginning to accept the concept and to reconcile it with their religions. One of the most important of the latter was the Reverend William Derham, who was successful in linking the science of the day with theology. In his book *Astro Theology, or a Demonstration of the Being and Attributes of God from a Survey of the Heavens*, Derham accepted the Copernican view of the cosmos—that the sun occupies the center of this planetary family—but only as a precursor to an idea he called his "New Systeme." In the New Systeme, Derham wrote:

> there are many other Systemes of Suns and Planets, besides that in which we have our residence; namely, that every Fixt Star is a sun and encompassed with a System of Planets, both Primary and Secondary as well as ours.

And it is this system, he argued, which is by

> far the most magnificent of any, and worthy of an infinite CREATOR . . .

During the first four decades of the 1700s, the concept of pluralism was winning international acceptance, and more than a dozen books were published on the subject. Astronomers no longer considered the idea to be mere speculation. In fact, they were beginning to believe that it was supported by observational evidence. For example, the moon's mountains and valleys appeared through a telescope as quite Earth-like. For all anyone knew, it might even have liquid water and life itself. Venus, by virtue of its cloudy atmosphere and similar size to Earth, led some to suspect it might be a planetary rain forest with creatures similar to those found in rain forests here. Of course, Mars's atmosphere and polar ice caps persuaded astronomers that, with surface temperatures similar to those of Earth, Mars must also be inhabited.

THE SEARCH BEGINS

One of the key astronomers of this period was the German-born Englishman Friedrich Wilhelm Herschel. William Herschel began his career as a music teacher and conductor but his consuming passion for astronomy eventually won out. During his lifetime, Herschel built some of the largest and best telescopes in the world—his largest was more than 6 meters long and supported a mirror about 30 centimeters across—which he used to catalog nearly all stars visible to the unaided eye, and in an attempt to measure the true shape of the Milky Way. In the spring of 1781, Herschel became the most famous astronomer in the world when he announced his discovery of the planet Uranus, the first "new" planet ever to be found.

The discovery of a new world took on vast importance to Herschel, whose work, it seems, was partly motivated by his belief that other worlds were inhabited. In fact, his extensive observations of the moon and planets of the solar system suggested to him that they were inhabited. While his observations never totally satisfied him—thus, he never published his manuscripts—Herschel believed that he had seen roads, buildings, and other artifacts of intelligent life on the moon.

Not only did Herschel suspect that the worlds of this solar system were populated, he also believed in the existence of planets in orbit around distant stars. Herschel recognized that every star

> is probably of as much consequence to a system of
> planets, satellites, and comets, as our own sun . . .

and that such planets

> can never be perceived by us.

Despite his realistic outlook, Herschel felt that he might gain some clues to their existence by studying certain stars carefully. One of his candidate objects was the star Algol in the constellation of Perseus. Today, Algol is widely known as a star that appears to vary in brightness as a companion star orbits in front and in back, causing eclipses to occur every three days. Why this variation should occur, however, was anyone's guess in Herschel's day. In 1783, Herschel advanced his own theory. He suggested that its changes in brightness could be explained if a planetary body were orbiting the star and occasionally passed between the Earth and the star. Not a bad guess, it turns out. If this theory were true, Herschel believed, it would verify the existence of a *"plurality of solar and planetary systems."*

Others of the period seemed determined to take things one step further—to understand not just the existence of planetary systems, but their origins as well. One of the most famous was a physically small man, but a philosophical giant: Immanuel Kant. From his hometown of Konigsberg, Germany, Kant gazed upward into the starry heavens and wondered where it all came from. He imagined the universe not as a simple collection of stars, but as millions of sources of heat and light that served the beings of countless worlds orbiting an infinite number of stellar systems in a nonstatic, evolving universe.

He wrote that, in an infinite and evolving universe, gravitational forces cause matter to condense around dense masses, gradually beginning to revolve around them and flatten into rings and individual spheres. In this way, he believed, galaxies, stars, and planetary systems came into being—each growing from the center outward. Since the core of each system was formed first, he argued, inhabitants there would be intellectually inferior to those who lived farther out. And he believed that all matter would eventually decay and die, and that this destruction would generate material to be recycled back into the construction of new worlds in the future.

POPULAR PLURALISM

By the middle of the eighteenth century, a new perspective on the universe was beginning to emerge. Astronomers were using large telescopes to scan the skies from horizon to horizon. Mathematical laws to describe the motions of the planets in orbit around the sun, and the moons in orbit about the planets, were well known and explained through Isaac Newton's theories of gravitation. The universe, it seemed, was as complex and orderly as anyone had ever imagined. And the concept of other worlds in orbit about other stars was sprouting everywhere.

One of the most popular writers of the day, Voltaire, wrote a story entitled "*Micromegas,*" which chronicled the adventures of a 36.6-kilometer-high nomadic inhabitant of a world orbiting the star Sirius. And the famous composer Ludwig van Beethoven wrote:

> . . . when in the evening I look up at the sky and see moving eternally in their worlds the host of bodies of light which are called suns and earths, then my mind soars beyond these many millions of distant stars to the one source from which new creations will eternally continue to stream.

Meanwhile, across the Atlantic, the idea was also catching hold in America. New schools such as Harvard and Yale were teaching about other suns and other worlds. In *Poor Richard's*

Almanac, authors were introducing the nonuniversity colonists to the idea of pluralism. One of the most famous of these was Benjamin Franklin, the leading American scientist of the day. In his *Articles of Belief,* Franklin stated:

> . . . when I stretch my Imagination thro' and beyond our System of Planets, beyond the visible fix'd Stars themselves, into that Space that is every Way infinite, and conceive it fill'd with Suns like ours, each with a Chorus of Worlds for ever moving round him then this little Ball on which we move, seems . . . to be almost Nothing, and my self less than nothing . . .

Franklin emphasized the physical smallness of the planet Earth in the grand scheme of the cosmos when, in 1757, he wrote of the recently predicted return of Halley's comet and speculated on a possible collision with the comet the following year:

> In the mean time, we must not presume too much on our own Importance. There are an infinite Number of Worlds under the Divine Government, and if this was annihilated it would scarce be miss'd in the Universe.

Even the future American president John Adams had the subject on his mind when he wrote in his diary on April 24, 1756:

> Astronomers tell us . . . that not only all the Planets and Satellites in our Solar System, but all the unnumbered Worlds that revolve round the fixt Starrs are inhabited . . . If this is the Case all Mankind are no more in comparison of the whole rational Creation of God, than a point to the Orbit of Saturn.

NOT EVERYONE'S A PLURALIST

The idea of pluralism continued to grow in popularity, partly because of the amazing astronomical discoveries and popular writings of the day, and partly because the concept was easily adaptable to any ideology and could be taught as well in the classroom as in the church. By the mid-nineteenth century, pluralism was being spread rapidly by astronomers and authors, by philosophers and poets. Nearly all educated people in Europe and the United States were convinced that most of the planets of the solar system, and probably even the moons of those planets, were inhabited. Few could doubt that even the farthest stars were the centers of inhabited planetary systems.

That's why, in 1853, the anonymously published book *On the Plurality of Worlds: An Essay,* shocked the world with its claim that many of the arguments in favor of other worlds were scientifically defective and religiously dangerous. It was even more of a shock when the book's author was disclosed to be William Whewell, a longtime supporter and defender of pluralism.

Born in Lancaster, England, Whewell was the son of a master carpenter. After his studies at Cambridge University, he was elected a fellow of Trinity College, Cambridge, in 1817. So strong was his belief in pluralism that he gave a powerful sermon on the subject at the University Church in 1827:

> . . . the earth . . . is one among a multitude of worlds . . . with resemblances and subordinations among them suggesting . . . that [they may be inhabited by] crowds of sentient . . . beings—these are not the reveries of idle dreamers or busy contrivers;—but, for the main part, truths collected by wise and patient men on evidence indisputable, from unwearied observation and thought; and for the rest, founded upon analogies which most will allow to reach at least to some degree of probability.

Six years later Whewell wrote a book entitled *Astronomy and General Physics Considered with Reference to Natural Theology,* in which he reasoned that the stars may

> . . . have planets revolving round them; and these may, like our planet, be the seats of vegetable and animal and rational life:—we may thus have in the universe worlds, no one knows how many, no one can guess how varied:—but however many, however varied, they are still but so many provinces in the same empire, subject to common rules, governed by a common power.

But in the intervening years, Whewell began to see problems with pluralism on both religious and scientific grounds. Over the next two decades he wrote very little on the subject, until he published his anonymous book in 1853. The thoughts within were driven mostly by his religious beliefs, even though he cleverly dismantled the pluralist ideas on both philosophical and scientific grounds.

More than half of Whewell's book consisted of scientific materials. He showed how the "observational" evidence of other inhabited worlds was weak at best, and how overextended analogies and bold interpretations of "the ways of God" created more problems than they solved. Whewell cautioned that before speculating on the existence and nature of other beings and lifeforms, astronomers must first *find the worlds* on which that life might exist.

According to Whewell, there was no evidence at all to support the notion that other worlds and other life existed. Double stars—pairs of stars that orbit a common center of gravity—he argued, would have too complex a gravitational field to support a planetary system. Variable stars, like Algol, which intrigued Herschel so, might change their brightnesses because of bodies eclipsing them periodically, but this effect would be visible only if those bodies were much larger than planetary size. The only stars that could possibly support planetary companions, he felt, were single, solar-type stars, and even they showed no direct evidence of planets.

With the majority of educated people now firmly believing in the existence of other worlds and other life, Whewell's *On the Plurality of Worlds: An Essay* was described by American professor of astronomy and mathematics Reverend Theodor Appel as "a bomb-shell thrown into an army resting on its victorious march." It became a virtual best-seller, and ran through at least five English and two American editions. By the end of the 1850s, it had generated more than fifty articles and reviews, twenty books, and countless letters, chapters, and other references by everyone from unknown writers to prominent scientific, theological, and literary figures of the day.

Whether correct or incorrect, Whewell's new antipluralist philosophy forced reality back into the equation at just the right time. According to Michael J. Crowe, "It seems that people had been overly prone to believe the planets were inhabited. Moreover, they had been overly prone to assume that other stars were going to have planets around them." Whewell's book demonstrated conclusively that one should not accept the notion blindly—no matter how popular—without indisputable scientific proof. And, while the book converted very few, it did force people to think critically about an issue they had always taken for granted, and focused upon it the spotlight of intense scientific inquiry.

A NEW ERA OF ASTRONOMY HAD BEGUN

The nineteenth century was a time of great technological innovation, when scientists began questioning the universe with newly invented tools. During this period, astronomers learned how to break a star's or planet's light into a finely detailed spectrum and read within it the chemical and physical properties of the body. They began to use triangulation, a common surveyor's mathematical tool, to measure the distance to the sun and stars.

They developed a technique for capturing light onto sensitized glass—photography, which made it possible to record their observations much more accurately and objectively and to preserve those observations for future generations to study. It was a time, as astronomer William Huggins stated, when:

> . . . nearly every observation revealed a new fact, and almost every night's work was red-lettered by some discovery.

It was an atmosphere of prolific discovery wherein new planets and planetary systems—if they existed at all—might be found. One who searched diligently for them was John Herschel, the only son of the great William Herschel. In 1833, in the *Royal Astronomical Society Memoirs*, he reported his belief that six double star systems might be places where the dimmer member of each pair was shining with reflected light, but stopped just short of calling them planets. In 1863, another well-respected astronomer with fourteen asteroid discoveries to his name, H. Goldschmidt, reported seeing five companions in orbit about the brilliant wintertime star Sirius. None were ever substantiated.

Another who believed strongly in the existence of extrasolar planets and was determined to find them was Dr. Thomas Jefferson Jackson See. In 1897, while an astronomer at the Lowell Observatory in Flagstaff, Arizona Territory, See announced some remarkable observations. He had been studying carefully the motions of double star systems, and wrote that he had found mathematical evidence that, in the system F70 Ophiuchus, a dark body appeared to be disturbing the regular elliptical motion of the stars:

> Our observations during 1896–97 have certainly disclosed stars more difficult than any which astronomers had seen before. Among these obscure objects about half a dozen . . . seem to be dark, almost black in color, and apparently

are shining by a dull, reflected light . . . If they should turn
out dark bodies in fact, shining only by the reflected light
of the stars around which they revolve, we should have
the first case of planets—dark bodies—noticed among the
fixed stars.

Astronomers from around the world responded to See's "discovery" by demolishing it on the basis of long-known scientific
facts—facts that had first been pointed out by Whewell more
than four decades earlier. They argued that unless the bodies
were far larger than Jupiter, they would appear far too dim and
much too small to be seen by even the most powerful telescopes
of the day.

ANOTHER WAVE OF POPULAR PLURALISM

Even though no planets or planetary systems had yet been confirmed by solid scientific evidence, the much wider subject of
astronomy was on the minds of many throughout the world. As
a result, the popular literature was teeming with astronomical
topics. Most responsible for this were two authors from two
widely separated continents: Richard Proctor and Camille Flammarion.

Proctor was one of the most prolific popular astronomical
writers of all time. In the twenty-five years between his first
publication and his sudden death in 1888, he authored fifty-
seven books and lectured in Britain, the United States, Canada,
Australia, and New Zealand. By the end of the 1800s, he was
without a doubt the most widely read author in the pluralist
debate. Yet, Proctor, being well versed in the sciences, believed
that the question of life on other worlds was

> . . . not a scientific question at all, belonging rather to the
> domain of philosophy than of science.

In making his case he presented an intriguing combination of analogy, religion, and science. And upon learning of the spectral evidence that other chemicals and metals exist in the stars, he wrote that

> the orbs circling around those distant suns are not meant merely to be the abode of life, but that intelligent creatures, capable of applying these metals to useful purposes, must exist in those worlds.

Proctor's book *Other Worlds than Ours,* written in 1870, treated the debate as completely as anyone had ever done. It became one of the most widely read books on the subject, going through at least twenty-nine printings between 1870 and 1909. In his 1877 book *Myths and Marvels of Astronomy,* Proctor wrote about how the newly developed spectroscopy and the improved telescopes of the time had only slightly changed scientists' view of other worlds.

> If men no longer imagine inhabitants of one planet because it is too hot, or of another because it is too cold, of one body because it is too deeply immersed in vaporous masses, or of another because it has neither atmosphere or water, we have only to speculate about the unseen worlds which circle round those other suns, the stars; or . . . we can look backward to the time when planets now cold and dead were warm with life, or forward to the distant future when planets now glowing with fiery heat shall have cooled down to a habitable condition.

The second author who captured the nineteenth-century public's imagination about other inhabited planetary systems was the Frenchman Camille Flammarion. Much like Proctor, Flammarion had an extensive scientific background; he authored more than seventy books, many of which were widely translated. His first book, *La Pluralité des Mondes Habités (The Plurality of*

Inhabited Worlds), was published in 1862 and, though merely a 54-page booklet, it landed him smack in the middle of the pluralist debate. Two years later he expanded the work to 570 pages, and he subsequently added a second, longer book, *Les Mondes Imaginaires et les Mondes Réels (Imaginary and Real Worlds).*

Pluralité was divided into three sections. In its historical section, Flammarion announced that ". . . the heroes of thought and of philosophy have ranged themselves under the banner which we are going to defend." In its second, and astronomical, section he concluded that ". . . the earth has no marked pre-eminence in the solar system of such a sort for it to be the only inhabited world." In the final section, Flammarion examined the possible physiology of the beings inhabiting other worlds, and warned readers not to assume that it was like their own lest one hurl "a gross insult in the shining face 'of the infinite Power who fashions the worlds."

The book was a tremendous success, partly due to the author's eloquent style and language, and partly because of the credibility lent by his scientific background. By 1870, when Richard Proctor's second book *Myths and Marvels of Astronomy,* was published, Flammarion's *Pluralité* was already in its fifteenth edition, on its way to a phenomenal forty editions with translations into some twenty languages, and his *Les Mondes* was in its ninth.

One of those translations was made in 1894 by the Irish engineer and astronomer John Ellard Gore, who also published his own book, *The Worlds of Space,* the same year. In his book, Gore logically presented his reasons for believing that other suns were home to planets: only those stars with spectra similar to that of the sun are probably similar in having planets; their great distances make these planets invisible to telescopes; and, since stars do not shine on *us,* they must have some other purpose. And he continued to use current star counts and probabilities to deduce that there must be "1,000,000 worlds in the *visible* universe fitted for the support of animal life."

The amazing technological advances and astronomical discoveries of the nineteenth century, along with the possible existence of other worlds, fired the imaginations of artists as well. They took what was known about the cosmos and extrapolated to the unknown, producing realistic paintings based on scientific facts and educated guesses. Not only did the "astronomical artists" of the nineteenth century re-create the landscapes of the Earth and its neighbors in the solar system, they also began to speculate about worlds beyond. In the process, they gave earthbound viewers a picture of the universe as never before.

REMOVING US FROM THE
CENTER . . . AGAIN

While the imaginations of the public and many astronomers were being captured by thoughts of other worlds and other life, some astronomers were working on other problems—one of which was so profound that its solution would change the way humans perceived themselves and the possibility of other worlds and life-forms within the universe. At the turn of the century, the American astronomer Harlow Shapley was using the 1.5-meter-diameter telescope of the Mt. Wilson Observatory in Southern California to study the positions of huge globes of thousands—even millions—of stars throughout the Milky Way.

Until the early years of the twentieth century, astronomers had only the vaguest of clues about the true nature of the Milky Way. The best guesses came from astronomers like William Herschel, who counted stars and estimated their size and shape. The best estimates at the time were that the Milky Way was a roughly lens-shaped system of stars 23,000 light-years long and 6,000 light-years thick, with the sun and Earth near its center. But simple cosmological models that place the Earth at the center never worked before, and Shapley was understandably uneasy about this description of the Milky Way.

This was more than just a gut feeling, for Shapley noticed that these globular star clusters could be seen in only half of the sky—the half that was visible to the Earth's Northern Hemisphere during summertime. Why these great star clusters should be spread so unevenly around the sky was anyone's guess, so Shapley decided to measure their distances to learn more about their physical distribution in the universe. To do so, he spent months searching the clusters for certain variable stars named Cepheids, which pulsated in rhythms that had long been known to correlate well with their distances. Shapley reasoned that if he could find Cepheid variables within a globular cluster, he could then determine not only the star's distance, but also that of the cluster in which it lay.

During the next few months, a staggering picture of the Milky Way began to emerge. The Milky Way, Shapley found, was a disk much larger than anyone had ever dreamed possible—perhaps more than twice the diameter previously suspected. More importantly, however, he discovered that the globular clusters formed a spherical halo above and below the Milky Way's plane. They did not appear symmetrical around the sky because the halo was centered about a point 10,000 light-years away, in the direction of the constellation Sagittarius—a point that marked the center of the Milky Way's disk. It turned out once again that the Earth was not located at the center. It, and the star it orbited, lay near the edge.

With this bold stroke of genius, Shapley accomplished what Copernicus dared to do some four and a half centuries earlier—he removed the Earth from the center of the universe. Our planet, it seemed, was in orbit around one single star—only one of a hundred billion that made up the Milky Way and that was far removed from its center. The Earth had lost its privileged position once again.

This suggested to many that if the sun—a normal-type star in the Milky Way—could have planets around it, then perhaps the billions of others out there could as well. The revolution in perspective had only begun for, around the same time, one of Shapley's colleagues at Mt. Wilson, Edwin P. Hubble, was also making news. Hubble was fascinated by the many curious nebulae found scattered among the stars—some appearing as delicate spirals, others elliptical, and still others with no definite shape at all. When Hubble used Cepheid variable stars to measure *their* distances, he found that they were not glowing clouds within the Milky Way as everyone had believed. They were instead island universes, giant Milky Ways in their own right, millions of light-years distant. The Milky Way, it seemed, was not the entire universe but merely one galaxy of many.

Then, in 1929, Hubble discovered an interesting pattern. All the galaxies seem to be rushing away from ours at speeds proportional to their distances. The farther away a galaxy was, the faster it was receding. If it was twice as far as another, it was moving twice as fast. If ten times farther, it was going ten times faster! He learned this by using a phenomenon first described by the Austrian physicist Christiaan Doppler in 1842.

Doppler suggested that light waves emanating from a moving object should appear different from those coming from a stationary object. To explain it more clearly, he offered an analogy with sound. A train whistle sounds higher in pitch while the train approaches because its sound waves are "squeezed" together. But as the train recedes, the sound waves are "stretched," and one perceives them as lower in pitch. Light behaves the same—not changing in pitch, but in color, turning bluer when an object approaches and redder when it recedes. Such color shifting is much too subtle to be seen unless an object is moving very rapidly and, even then, requires precise measurements of specific features within the object's spectrum. Any spectral lines that appear shifted toward the blue end of the spectrum from where they "should" appear for a stationary object emitting the same spectrum indicate a velocity of approach proportional to the amount of shift, while any features that appear red-shifted indicate a velocity of recession for the body.

This is just what Hubble found. With the exception of some of the nearest of galaxies, all were rushing *away* from *us*. Was it possible, after all, that the Milky Way galaxy was indeed in the center of the entire universe? Was Hubble seeing some grand design—similar to those that had been proved incorrect time and time again? Or was the Milky Way at the center because of some bizarre cosmic coincidence? None of these scenarios were acceptable to Hubble, and so he reasoned that the galaxies were not rushing away from ours, but from each other, as if from a colossal explosion billions of years ago: the big bang. Since every galaxy is rushing away from every other galaxy, an observer in the universe—no matter where he or she happens to be—would perceive the same phenomenon: all galaxies would be rushing away.

With their observations, Shapley and Hubble had done what Copernicus and Galileo had done a few centuries earlier. They had reduced the physical significance of the Earth world in the cosmic scheme of things, and changed humanity's perspectives one more time. They demonstrated conclusively that Earth did not occupy a special and privileged position, that this world was only a tiny planet in orbit around a tiny star in an insignificant galaxy somewhere in a universe billions of light-years across. By doing so, they showed that other worlds were just as likely to exist as ours—anywhere in the universe.

For ages, the debate has continued to rage. Are we alone or are we not? Could a "Creator" create other planets and other life-forms? And if He could, would He? But now, after all was said and done, one thing had become abundantly clear: the planet known as Earth was a physically insignificant speck in a vast and unimaginably large cosmos. If it occupied such an un-privileged position in the cosmos, then perhaps it was not all that unique. Perhaps the existence of other worlds and other life-forms was not that far-fetched after all. Astronomers were definitely primed for a discovery.

2

FIRST CLUES

The first half of the twentieth century saw astronomical discoveries come at a prodigious rate. Astronomers learned that the Milky Way was part of an immense universe of galaxies that were racing apart as if hurled from a huge cosmic fireball perhaps 15 billion years ago. They found that the universe radiates in wavelengths not visible to the human eye—infrared, radio, and X rays—and that special instruments could be built to detect these signals. They also learned of the existence of a ninth planet in the solar system—Pluto—a world so distant and faint that its light was detected only after an intense nine-month search. With an entirely new universe coming into view, it seemed that the discovery of planets and planetary systems in orbit around *other* stars could not be far behind.

Therefore, on April 18, 1963, at an astronomical conference in Tucson, Arizona, when the distinguished astronomer Dr. Peter Van de Kamp of Swarthmore College's Sproul Observatory stood before the media with news of yet another discovery, the imagination of the world was piqued. It was here that Van de Kamp announced his discovery of a new planet. But *this* planet was unlike any that had ever been found before, for it was nine thousand times more distant than Pluto, and orbiting another star.

MOVING STARS

Van de Kamp's discovery came about in a rather indirect way. He never actually *saw* the planet itself but, instead, deduced its presence mathematically. For two and a half decades he had watched the irregular movement of its parent star across the nighttime sky, and he determined that only through the gravitational tugging of an orbiting planet could the star appear to wobble as it did.

That stars move at all came as a surprise to most people. Certainly the stars seem to drift slowly from east to west during the course of a night, but this is merely an illusion caused by the spinning of the Earth on its axis every twenty-four hours. Their patterns do change from season to season as well; for example, the constellation Orion shines brightly in the southern sky every winter evening, but by summer it can be seen only in the eastern sky before dawn. This, too, can be attributed to the motion of the Earth: it is caused by the annual journey of this world around the sun, enabling sky watchers to see outward in different directions during the course of a year.

But what about the stars themselves? They never seem to move in relation to each other. Orion is always Orion, Scorpius is always Scorpius—no matter what season or year or century it is. In fact, the stars are so static that the constellations visible tonight are the same as those watched by stargazers millennia ago. We know this because astronomers have measured for centuries the positions of stars in the sky, and have watched carefully for any movement. Never did they find any—until 1718, that is.

In that year, a remarkable discovery was made by Sir Edmond Halley, best known for mathematically predicting the return of the famous comet that now bears his name. However, it was not comets that intrigued Halley on that night. Instead, it was his discovery that the bright stars Sirius and Arcturus were not exactly in the positions tabulated by the ancient astronomer Claudius Ptolemaeus—or Ptolemy. Granted they were off by only the tiniest fraction of a degree, but Halley knew that Ptolemy was not one to have made such an error. Was it possible that the two stars had actually moved since Ptolemy's time? To find out, Halley began to measure their positions very carefully. He soon found that these stars were, in fact, moving ever so slowly through the sky.

It was not long before astronomers learned that other stars moved, too, and that a star's "proper motion" was inversely related to its distance. In other words, a nearby star seemed to move more rapidly than one farther away. This effect is known to anyone who has ever ridden in a car. When one drives down the highway, the nearest of trees seem to whip by, while those in the distance seem almost still. Watch long enough, however, and the positions of distant trees can seem to change. The speed of the car past both is the same—it's just that the farther trees take much longer to show their relative motions.

The stars, too, are whipping by at incredible speeds. Most are so distant that millennia must pass before their movement becomes obvious. The Big Dipper, for example, is made of seven stars that form the familiar shape of a pot with a bent handle. Its five central stars are bound to a cluster 75 light-years away, and they move together in a similar direction at similar speeds. Two stars in the Dipper, however, are not part of that cluster and experience their own individual motions: Alkaid, at the end of the Dipper's handle, and Dubhe, at the far corner of its bowl. Since each star of this figure has its own proper motion, the Dipper is constantly changing, but thousands of years will pass before its familiar shape becomes distorted beyond recognition.

A WOBBLING STAR

As stars move through space they must obey the laws of motion first described by Isaac Newton in the eighteenth century. Newton stated that a body in motion must move in a straight path unless it is influenced by an outside force. In other words, a single star moving through the emptiness of space must travel in a perfectly straight path. In 1844, though, astronomer Friedrich Wilhelm Bessel found a more complex and intriguing situation.

In that year, Bessel discovered that the bright wintertime stars Sirius and Procyon were not traveling along a straight path, but seemed to wobble slightly as they moved. If Newton's laws were correct, it occurred to Bessel, something must be tugging on these stars and making them wobble. He diligently searched the region around them for other stars whose gravity might be disrupting their motion and found absolutely nothing. Judging from the motions of the stars, Bessel concluded that each must have a companion orbiting nearby, but one much fainter than he could see with his telescopes.

The motion of the "binary" stars, as Bessel found out, was not unlike that which might be observed in a playground here on Earth. Imagine two children riding a seesaw. To keep it balanced, they must place the fulcrum at the board's center of mass. If the children each weigh the same, that point would lie in the middle of the board and the children would each get a similar ride up and down. But if a child were riding with a heavier person, let's say a parent, the center of mass would lie much closer to the parent. As they ride, the child would travel a wildly swinging path up and down, while the parent would just bounce slightly. If the ride were adjusted so that, instead of only bouncing up and down, the riders could swing around completely, the heavier parent (closer to the fulcrum) would trace out a tiny circle about the center of mass, while the lighter child would "orbit" in a much wider circle.

Now suppose the entire mechanism could be moved horizontally on a track. As it moves by, an outside observer would see the center of mass of the seesaw—the point about which the board is mounted—glide smoothly by on a straight path, but the riders would each trace out a completely different path. The lighter child would seem to oscillate wildly above and below the track as he swings around, while the heavier parent would appear only to wobble up and down slightly. From the period and size of this oscillation an observer could infer the child's existence, calculate his distance from the parent, and learn his mass or weight—even if he were too tiny to be seen.

The same is true of stars. As a single star moves through space, Newton's laws of motion dictate that it must move in a straight path. If, on the other hand, it is accompanied by another body, only their center of mass will travel in a straight path. Each star will oscillate back and forth as it moves—the heavier it is, the less it will seem to oscillate—and just as with the seesaw, if one of the companions is not visible, its presence can still be deduced by the wobbles it causes in the primary star.

Such gravitational perturbations of stars are very small at most—only the tiniest fraction of a degree. Because the stars are very distant, their motions take many decades to detect, even with long-focus optical telescopes such as the 1-meter-diameter refractor at the Yerkes Observatory or the 0.9-meter refractor at the Lick Observatory. To assure accuracy and consistency of data, astronomers must refrain from making optical adjustments to the equipment over many years or decades.

The process of "astrometry," the measure of stellar positions and motions, goes like this. At the focal plane of a telescope, astronomers gather light onto large glass photographic plates to keep the image quality stable and prevent the photo from being bent or distorted. Each is marked and calibrated and, from hundreds or thousands of plates of the same stars spanning many decades, astronomers can measure stellar positions with a precision equivalent to one-hundredth the width of a human hair. The data are then plotted to illustrate the star's changing position, along with bars to graphically show the margin of error in the data. If the star has an unseen stellar companion large enough to cause detectable perturbations of its motion, its path will appear as a wavy line.

In principle, it is all very simple. In practice, any perturbations detected in a star's path will always be complicated by the Earth, and astronomers must be careful to remove the Earth's influence from the data before they can determine with certainty the presence of an unseen companion.

One such complicating factor is the annual trip of the Earth around the sun. As the Earth circles the sun in its multimillion-kilometer orbit, observers look out upon the stars from different angles. In the springtime, one sees the stars from one side of the Earth's orbit; six months later, one views them from the opposite side. To astronomers with sensitive detectors, the nearest stars seem to shift their positions back and forth against the more distant stars. An unsuspecting observer might interpret the oscillating motion of these stars as evidence of an unseen companion lurking near the stars. The phenomenon is much like looking out a window at a distant landscape while moving your head slowly in a small circle. A housefly walking across the glass will appear to trace a small circle or ellipse against the more distant landscape as you move your head. The true path of the housefly—whether a straight path or a wobbling motion—is distorted by the motion of your own head.

Another problem is that the sun is tearing along through its stellar neighborhood in the direction of the bright summertime star Vega at a speed of some 19 kilometers per second, with the Earth and its planetary family in tow. Imagine trying to measure accurately the path of the housefly as you move your head in a circle while walking across the room and you get some idea of the problem's complexity.

Fortunately, the motions of the Earth are predictable enough that they can be subtracted out of the data. Once that is done, a star's path might appear as a straight line—or a tiny wobble might remain. Year after year, decade after decade, a graph of a star's motion is slowly generated. If it shows a wobble that is larger than the inherent errors, scientists can conclude that the star has a companion. From the period and size of the perturbation, they can deduce its mass and its distance from the primary star.

Through this demanding and time-consuming process, several

dozen "astrometric binary" stars have been discovered—stars whose paths seem to wobble, thereby suggesting the presence of an unseen companion tugging gravitationally on them. Most of the companions detected seem to be tiny stars much too faint to be seen over the glare of their primary star. One of the most intriguing, however, was a small, obscure star in the summertime constellation of Ophiuchus. Its name was Barnard's Star.

AN UNUSUAL CANDIDATE

Barnard's Star was named for the American who discovered it in 1916. It happened when Edward Emerson Barnard, an astronomer at the Yerkes Observatory in Williams Bay, Wisconsin, was comparing a photograph of the stars in the region of the constellation Ophiuchus with one taken twenty-two years earlier. As he studied the two plates, Barnard noticed that one faint star seemed out of place: it was not where it had appeared twenty-two years earlier. Barnard learned that between the times the two plates were taken this star had apparently moved northward by nearly 4 minutes of arc—one-eighth of the diameter of the full moon. A star that moved so far so quickly was no ordinary star.

Barnard soon made another discovery. The star was barely 6 light-years away and was the closest star visible from Earth's Northern Hemisphere, but the star shined so dimly that it could be seen only with a powerful telescope. The only way this could be, he deduced, was if the star were tiny and faint. By comparison, if moved to that distance, the sun would shine some 2,230 times brighter and would remain one of the brighter stars in the sky. The reason that Barnard's Star appeared so faint, it turned out, is that it is a red dwarf star, five times less massive and half as hot as the sun. Its tiny size and fast motion suggested that this star might be easily swayed by an unseen companion, and that made it a perfect candidate for such a search.

When Van de Kamp took over the directorship of the Sproul Observatory in 1937, he began a unique observing program with the 0.6-meter refractor telescope. His goal was to monitor the motions of tiny nearby stars over a long time period to improve the accuracy of distance measurements, and to search their motions for the telltale wobbling signs of unseen companions. Near the top of his observing list was the peculiar star known as Barnard's Star. Perhaps it would finally reveal an unseen companion.

Of course, such work had been done before, but Van de Kamp hoped that he would detect more than just small companion *stars*. "Peter decided to put a new slant on this work," recalls one of Van de Kamp's earliest graduate students, Sarah Lee Lippincott, who became the director of Sproul Observatory following Van de Kamp's retirement in 1981. "As a by-product, or perhaps as the main thrust, he hoped this search might lead to the discovery of planetary companions."

Whether something as tiny as a planet could ever be found was not known. In fact, no one at the time even knew how massive an object could be and still be considered a planet rather than a star. "We all knew that Jupiter was the most massive planet in *our* solar system," recalls Lippincott, "but what would be the limiting mass *elsewhere*? Gradually, it became clear that it was something around one-twentieth of a solar mass." If a body this small were tugging gravitationally on a star, the tiny perturbations it would cause would require extremely accurate work and technology to detect.

To do such fine work, Van de Kamp chose to use the 0.6-meter long-focus refractor at Sproul. "He started to concentrate on stars out to about twenty or thirty light-years," says Lippincott, "but the most intensive study went to those stars between ten and twenty light-years away because he thought the nearest ones would be those that would show the largest deviation from linear proper motion. Whether an unseen companion would have a mass low enough to qualify as a planetary object—well, that was unknown at the time."

Van de Kamp knew that results from this study would not come quickly, and that many years of research and accurate data reduction might be necessary before enough data were available for him to make valid conclusions about the existence of unseen companions. So two to three nights a month, Van de Kamp and his colleagues aimed the Sproul refractor toward the stars and exposed from eight to sixteen photographic plates to the light of their target stars. Then the astronomers would examine the plates and measure the target stars' positions relative to three presumably stationary reference stars, calculate and remove the effects of the Earth's motions, average the measurements for each night, and plot the stars' average positions on a graph. If this weren't enough, the seemingly endless stream of numbers required for accurate results was cranked out on hand-operated measuring devices and mechanical calculators.

Surprisingly, it was within only a few years that Van de Kamp and his associates began to see some interesting results. They found what he believed was a tiny twenty-four-year oscillation in the proper motion of the star—perhaps the result of an unseen companion orbiting Barnard's Star every two dozen years. Still, Van de Kamp knew that he could only hope to confirm his suspicions by gathering data over the entire twenty-four-year period—so he did just that. Month after month, year after year, Van de Kamp photographed the star, measured its position, and plotted it on a graph over time.

During the next quarter century, Van de Kamp's devotion to his observing project became legendary. So did his other interests, which delighted him during the long and grueling process. One of those who recalled with fondness his other passions is the late Robert Harrington, a former graduate student of Van de Kamp and an astronomer at the United States Naval Observatory in Washington, D.C.

"Van de Kamp was really popular on campus. The reason was that his hobby was collecting silent comedy movies, principally those of Charlie Chaplin. Every Wednesday evening, we'd have a Charlie Chaplin seminar where he'd pull out one or two of these movies and show them over at the student union. And once a year, for the college movie we'd get in an old silent Douglas Fairbanks feature—something like *Robin Hood* or *The*

Mark of Zorro, and Van de Kamp would play the piano accompaniment live. He was a great piano player. Not only that, but Van de Kamp conducted the [college] orchestra for many years, and he was also a member of a string quartet. The other three people were over at Princeton. One of them was Albert Einstein."

THE ANNOUNCEMENT

By 1963, after measuring the position of Barnard's Star on thousands of plates, Van de Kamp felt he had the data he needed to make a conclusion. "It seemed pretty obvious that the star was showing some deviations in proper motion which could be attributed to a companion with a very low mass," recalls Lippincott. But his announcement of the find did not come easily. "I know he had many soul-searching talks with Martin Schwarzschild at the time," she recalls. "Schwarzschild, a very reputable and strong astronomer, told him that, if he really thought there was a good possibility [that the results were good], then he should announce it."

That's just what Van de Kamp decided to do. On the eighteenth of April, 1963, he announced to the world that Barnard's Star was orbited by an unseen companion only half again as heavy as Jupiter. Van de Kamp proclaimed himself to be the first to discover a planet in orbit around another star.

The world he described was strange indeed: a body larger than Jupiter orbiting a red star smaller than the sun. And, though Van de Kamp had never actually *seen* the world itself, his calculations convinced him that the planet orbited the star not in a near-circle like the orbits of planets in the Solar System, but in a highly elongated one—more like a comet. The world apparently spent most of its orbit more than a billion kilometers from its star, but at times approached to less than 322 million kilometers.

"This [announcement] made quite a flurry at the time, I remember," recalls Lippincott. Newspaper, radio, and television reporters descended in droves on Van de Kamp and on the tiny

Pennsylvania campus. Everyone wanted to talk to the man who discovered the first planet in orbit around an alien sun. Based on astronomers' accepted understanding of how the Earth's family of planets had formed, many soon began to speculate about whether this newly discovered planet might not be part of an entire system of planets—most of whose members were much too small for their gravitational effects on the star to be detected. Yet, for all the media hype of 1963, Van de Kamp knew that, in order to refine his data and make stronger conclusions, he must continue his research.

By 1968, he announced that his study of the position of Barnard's Star on 3,036 photographic plates suggested that the body—now believed to be perhaps 1.7 times as massive as Jupiter—seemed to be orbiting the star with a period of twenty-five years, and in an even more eccentric orbit than he had once believed. Then, a year later, he proposed an even more startling possibility, that the star's wobbling motion could be explained not only by a single planet of 1.7 Jupiter masses orbiting every twenty-five years, but also by *two* bodies in circular coplanar orbits. One, he proposed, was 1.1 times the mass of Jupiter and orbiting with a twenty-six-year period; the other, orbiting closer to the star every twelve years, might have a mass of 0.8 Jupiters.

If Van de Kamp's 1963 announcement came as a surprise, this was an even greater one. Only a few years earlier, no extrasolar planets had ever been detected. Now, it seemed, there was potentially an entire system of worlds orbiting Barnard's Star.

WHAT KINDS OF WORLDS?

The announcement by Van de Kamp invited—even begged for—all kinds of speculation. What types of worlds were orbiting Barnard's Star? Were there any like Earth? Was it possible that some might be home to life—perhaps even intelligent life? Astronomers soon began to use their knowledge of stars to consider the possibilities.

The type of planets, perhaps even the number of planets, that a star might have depends on what kind of star it is. Here, the sun is a mixture of lighter elements—hydrogen and helium—and heavier elements such as silicon, oxygen, and iron. The material out of which the sun and planetary family were formed presumably contained all of these elements, and it was from these that both the rocky and gaseous planets came into being. By studying the chemical signatures within the spectrum of Barnard's Star, however, astronomers knew that this star was quite different from the Earth's.

First, with a temperature and diameter barely half that of the sun, Barnard's Star seemed to be composed of an abundance of light elements like hydrogen and helium, but few that are heavier. It seemed likely, then, that if the planetary system around this star formed in the same way as did ours (and there was no reason to suspect otherwise), then the worlds of Barnard's Star might be mostly gaseous giants like Jupiter and Saturn. Rocky worlds like Earth might be scarce or, perhaps, even nonexistent. Secondly, astronomers recognized that although the two suspected planets were calculated to orbit the star with roughly the same periods as Jupiter and Saturn, the weaker gravitational pull of their tiny parent star would require them to orbit much closer in.

Either way, planets orbiting this tiny, cool star seemed most likely to be cold, gas giants, perhaps much like Jupiter and Saturn. Even though some astronomers had severe doubts about the data and their interpretation, the implications of the announcement extended far beyond the rather elite world of astrometrists. They touched the imagination of the public, school children, and other scientists as well. After all, it seemed, Van de Kamp had accomplished something about which our ancestors could only dream—finding planets around a distant sun.

* * *

THE PLOT THICKENS

One evening shortly after Van de Kamp's announcement of his two-planet theory, Robert Harrington sat in his apartment reading two research papers from the Sproul Observatory when he made a discovery that would ultimately erode his confidence in the data of his former mentor. "I found that the plots of the perturbations for two stars—Barnard's Star and another one—looked deceptively similar. So I ran back up to the office and plotted all of the Sproul perturbations and discovered that there was a common feature."

The feature that had so intrigued Harrington was a strange discontinuity in the stars' motion—a discontinuity that appeared in all data Van de Kamp had taken of the two stars around 1949. Was this discontinuity a real phenomenon? If so, why did it appear in the data taken for *both* stars at the same time, and *only* in the data gathered at the Sproul Observatory? Harrington was convinced that this discontinuity could not be a real astrophysical phenomenon, and suspected that it was caused not by an orbiting planet tugging on the star, but by a change in the telescope optics themselves.

The telescope Van de Kamp had been using gathered and focused light by way of lenses in a sealed tube, rather than by mirrors in the open air. Such "refractor" telescopes are much more rugged than "reflectors," and seldom need to have their lenses removed for repair or refurbishment. Since removing and replacing a lens can introduce systematic errors into the positions of stars on a photographic plate, refractors have long been recognized as ideal for performing precision work over years or decades of time. Still, even refractors need to be cleaned occasionally, and that's just what happened at Sproul in 1949.

Now for most types of astrometric work, the errors introduced by removing and replacing a lens might not make much difference, but for the accuracy required by Van de Kamp, the new optical alignment was off just enough to cause a problem, and a serious one at that. When the data were compared with those taken *before* the change, the discontinuity appeared in the paths of the stars' motions and produced the illusion of wobbles—wobbles that Van de Kamp had interpreted as evidence of extrasolar planets.

With two decades of data now seriously suspect, no one would have blamed Van de Kamp for throwing his hands in the air and giving up completely. But the good professor was hardly the type to concede defeat just because one serious error threatened to destroy a lifetime of work. So, with typical determination and patience, he put away all photographic plates he had taken before 1950 and continued to gather data on the stars. His goal now was to gather data until he could confidently make another conclusion—this time *without* the use of pre-1950 plates.

Through all those years and all those measurements, Dr. Lippincott worked closely by his side. "By [the late seventies] we could do away with the material [from before] 1950," she recalls. "We felt confident that the [data] after fifty was pretty consistent for all stars, and that any deviation we could find would probably not be spurious or systematic, but would be real. But again, the deviation we found was very, very small."

It was from these tiny deviations that Van de Kamp in 1978 announced his new findings. He again described two bodies in orbit around Barnard's star—one with a mass of 0.8 Jupiters orbiting every 11.7 years in a nearly circular orbit some 400 million kilometers out, and the other with a mass of 0.4 Jupiters orbiting every 20 years or more at a distance of 568 million kilometers. Three years later, he revised his figures further: the unseen companions now measured 0.7 Jupiters orbiting every 12 years, and 0.5 Jupiters with a period of 20 years. Van de Kamp was as convinced as ever that he had enough data to confidently claim discovery of the first extrasolar planets in history.

*   *   *

MORE CHALLENGES AHEAD

Van de Kamp had his challengers. Astronomers around the United States had begun to look carefully at photographic plates of Barnard's Star taken with other telescopes for signs of indisputable wobbling. One of the first, and most damaging, tests came from a most unlikely candidate: George Gatewood, now of the Allegheny Observatory in Pittsburgh.

Gatewood entered the Barnard's Star planetary search by the back door. While a graduate student working on his master's degree at the University of Virginia, he began to study the Leander McCormick refractor telescope, which apparently had been suffering some optical problems of its own. At the conclusion of his study, he continued his master's degree work at the University of South Florida and undertook a similar calibration for all other telescopes involved in astrometric research, including the 1.5-meter reflector at the United States Naval Observatory (USNO) in Flagstaff, Arizona.

Upon completing his project, Gatewood came to a remarkable realization. "I said to myself, this is one hell of a Ph.D. dissertation project! A year later, I had my master's degree from USF. So I took this thing, put it in boxes, and took it to the University of Pittsburgh and the Allegheny Observatory." It was there that Gatewood began his studies under an astronomer named Joost Kiewiet DeJonge, who, years earlier, had roomed with Van de Kamp, and harbored some serious doubts about the Barnard's Star work.

"After a year [at Allegheny], DeJonge came to me and said, 'You ought to make the study of Barnard's Star your Ph.D. dissertation,' " recalls Gatewood. "I said, 'No, I don't want to do that.' 'Why not?,' he replied. 'Well, I don't really care whether Barnard's Star has a planet around it or not. That'll all come out later on. Right now, I'd rather do *this* study,' because, of course, I had it all done already. About three months later, DeJonge came to me again and said, 'I really think you ought to do this as your dissertation—the study of Barnard's

Star—to see if it has a companion.' And I said, 'Well, I know Peter Van de Kamp and I admire him, and I think the work he's done is very good, and I really would rather do this *other* project.' The third time he came to me was only about two weeks later. When I started objecting again he said very quietly, 'You *do* want to graduate, don't you?' Suddenly I saw his point of view. And that's how I was launched onto the study of Barnard's Star."

Gatewood had first met Van de Kamp some years earlier while the astronomer was visiting Sarasota to discuss possibly studying with him at Swarthmore. "I was to meet him at his motel on the beach," recalls Gatewood, "this early 1900-like building sitting amongst the tall pine trees. It looked like something out of a Humphrey Bogart film. When I found his room, he wasn't there and, as I was writing him a note, this man came up to me wearing—honest to God—a swimming outfit which included a T-shirt like [those] from the early part of the century. It was Peter Van de Kamp! This was the man who later, over a hamburger and a Coke, told me he checked his calculators with logarithms to make sure they were right! The man was just full of personality—and a very, very delightful fellow."

Despite his enormous admiration for the great astronomer, Gatewood knew he must perform his work objectively, and it didn't take long for him to realize that something was wrong with Van de Kamp's data. Gatewood had written a program to perform a simple line plot of the data and, as it printed slowly and methodically from the large, centralized computer, he sat talking with another student while trying unsuccessfully to contain his excitement. "Suddenly I saw one come out with a beautiful perturbation," he recalls. "This was the Barnard's Star field, and I literally ran over to the printer so I could be close. Sure enough the perturbation was three-hundredths of an arc second—thirty milli-arcseconds—a *huge* perturbation by today's standards. Nicely shaped, absolutely impressive. And I said to someone, 'Look, there it is! There's the perturbation!' "

But then, Gatewood noticed something strange. Barnard's

Star appeared to be moving not only in one direction, but in a second as well. After some investigation, Gatewood concluded that this second perturbation was caused by Van de Kamp's fourth reference star—a presumably static star from which he measured the positions of Barnard's Star—which was itself moving about. "Almost immediately I wrote a letter to Van de Kamp saying that his fourth reference star had a perturbation and, since he never studied those things, he [never realized the problem]."

Through the years, Gatewood and his colleagues continued to study the motion of Barnard's Star. In 1973, they gathered 241 photographic plates of the star taken with other telescopes. Eighty were from the 0.5-meter Van Vleck refractor from 1923 to 1971, and 161 were from the Allegheny 0.8-meter refractor from 1916 to 1971. Because they had nowhere near as many plates as Van de Kamp used, they were forced to improve the accuracy of their work by other methods. For example, they examined the plates with the highly accurate semiautomatic measuring engine of the U.S. Naval Observatory, and they measured the position of the star relative not to three reference stars, as Van de Kamp did, but to a network of nineteen separate stars.

Through these new techniques their results soon became comparable in accuracy to those of Van de Kamp, even though they used only one-tenth the number of photographic plates. "The motion that Van de Kamp had found was plus or minus three-hundredths of an arc second—and he had taken thousands of plates to get that," explains Gatewood. "The error of a single observation on a single plate for the larger Allegheny telescope, which was measured on a more accurate measuring machine and reduced with a more elegant algorithm, was also three-hundredths of an arc second. So, theoretically, you could see this perturbation with a single photographic plate."

Gatewood recalls his findings from hundreds of plates and many hours of measurements and data reduction: "The motion of Barnard's Star was linear to within the error of the study." When their results appeared in print, he and his colleagues wrote sadly: "We conclude with disappointment that our observations fail to confirm the existence of a planetary companion to Barnard's Star."

Certainly Gatewood wasn't the first to dispute Van de Kamp's data. "There were a lot of people who didn't believe in the planet before I got there, [and] they had already begun to point out that it was something the man was doing to his telescope." He was not the last, either.

Astronomers at the University of Virginia's Leander McCormick Observatory, after using highly accurate measuring machines to determine stellar positions on photographic plates and processing these with accurate mathematical analysis, found something strange. They announced their results in 1985; unfortunately, it was not good news. They, too, saw no evidence that Barnard's Star had planets around it. If it had been wobbling in the east-west direction, as Van de Kamp had recorded all those years, their telescope never picked it up. What they did see, however, was a perturbation in the *north-south* direction that included a "jump" in 1977. Why the Virginia researchers missed what Van de Kamp had seen, and saw what Van de Kamp had missed, was indeed a mystery.

Meanwhile, astronomers at the U.S. Naval Observatory were also at work on the project. Van de Kamp's former student Robert Harrington and his colleagues were using the 1.5-meter reflector at the USNO station in Flagstaff, Arizona, to measure the parallaxes of a thousand nearby stars—the slight displacements these stars undergo as a result of viewing them from slightly different angles at widely spaced points along the Earth's orbit—and using these to calculate the stars' distances. Unlike the Sproul Observatory's "Coke-bottle refractor," as Harrington jokingly called it, the 1.5-meter instrument was designed specifically for measuring stellar positions and was, therefore, three to five times more accurate, depending on the measuring machine one used to measure the plates.

When Harrington took over the USNO parallax program, he asked his boss, Dr. Kaj Strand, if he could put Barnard's Star on his observing list. "He said, 'No we couldn't, because too many people had wasted too much time on [it] already," he recalled. "So we put it on anyway and didn't tell him. When Strand retired, we shipped the plates that we had collected from Flagstaff to Washington and started measuring the thing. I guess [by then] we had gotten eighteen or nineteen years' worth of data [on Barnard's Star]."

From these, Harrington was able to show that Barnard's Star did not follow the path predicted by Van de Kamp but, instead, one strikingly similar to that found by the Virginia team: no east-west wobble, a tiny, but possible, north-south perturbation, and the same "jump" in the north-south direction in 1977. The astronomers, so tantalizingly close to evidence of a planetary system in orbit around Barnard's Star, could make no definite conclusions. "I could never say unequivocally that [Van de Kamp's] perturbation does not exist," explained Harrington. "It's still small enough that it could be hidden away in the data. It's just that my data is represented a whole lot better with a straight line than it is with his curve. So I think that our initial doubts [about his results] that came from the late sixties have unfortunately been borne out."

Over the years, an increasing number of astronomers have become skeptical of Van de Kamp's work. Sarah Lee Lippincott, Van de Kamp's longtime assistant, views it all philosophically. "I have no doubt that anyone using our material in detail might very likely come up with the same conclusion as we have. And likewise, if we had used somebody else's material exclusively, we would have probably come up with their interpretation. If the scientist is good, this may very well happen." But, in the face of intense scientific rebuttal, Lippincott still defends the life-long research performed by the group at Sproul. "Indeed, there were many stars that really didn't show any deviations, and when you look over years, [their paths] were terribly smooth and con-sistent. These gave credence to the trends we found in Barnard's Star or any other."

Today, of course, Lippincott is in the minority. Many believe that the planets Van de Kamp detected around Barnard's Star were merely an illusion—an effect of less than perfect optics, inefficient measurement techniques, and, perhaps, an overly enthusiastic desire to find planets in the first place. Yet, despite the number of negative results that have come from around the astronomical community, few, if any, astronomers really enjoyed disproving the work of the great professor.

"Van de Kamp was a nice, old grandfatherly type," said Harrington. "I always liked him. He was a really nice guy and I feel very bad that I had to be the one to say to him that his discovery hasn't been borne out." Gatewood couldn't agree more. "To me the man was rather a king, and I wasn't rushing out to find these things. The perturbations were so large that when you take several hundred observations and put them together, you improve the precision. And I was absolutely convinced that the planets weren't there.

"I experienced such a mixture of feelings," recalls Gatewood. "You know, on the one hand it was some excitement that I was going to confirm this planetary system, and a disappointment when I didn't find it. And I [felt somewhat] sad that I showed the man's work to be wrong. It's kind of a shame, too, because he did an incredible amount of good work. He kind of hung his entire reputation on one star. And he was just wrong on it."

THE WORK CONTINUES

Decades after it first made headlines, Barnard's Star continues to excite and confound. "Back in '89 or so," recalls Gatewood, "I walked into a meeting late, and saw Bob Harrington showing a plot of Barnard's Star. He had this beautiful dip somewhere in the mid-eighties in [its north-south] motion. I was carrying slides that showed a [north-south] dip during the same year. I got all excited and thought 'maybe there's something here after all!' "

At the end of the talk, Harrington and Gatewood went out for a beer and began to discuss the apparent similarities of their work. They discovered that there did appear in both their data a dip in the mid-1980s, but one was three times larger than the other. If planets were tugging on Barnard's Star at this time, both telescopes would have recorded the motion in the same way, so the astronomers began to suspect that the two had little, if anything, to do with each other. Then, as Gatewood and Harrington were finishing their beers, another Barnard's Star researcher happened to wander by their table. "We asked if he had found anything [during the mid-eighties] and he said, 'Nope, not a thing. No motion,'" recalled Gatewood. "So we decided that it was very unlikely that the dip was anything more than a random coincidence. What do they say? 'In a chaotic universe, coincidence is an absolute certainty.'"

DOES BARNARD HAVE PLANETS OR NOT?

What does all this contradictory evidence say about the existence of a planetary system around Barnard's Star? Does it mean that no planets orbit the star after all? Does it mean that Barnard has planets that tug noticeably on the star only at certain times? Or, perhaps, planets that are so tiny that their gravitational effects are beyond the ability of Earth-bound observers to detect, and that all we have seen so far are merely artifacts of optics and technology? Though the astronomers have never found Van de Kamp's now-famous wobble, they have found others that keep the dream alive. Even though some astronomers still debate the existence of planets around Barnard's Star, one has remained absolutely certain about the issue—the man who started it all: Peter Van de Kamp.

Van de Kamp's conviction was never more clear than in a 1983 talk he gave at Wesleyan University. In it he spoke of his "dear old friend, Barnard's Star." After presenting his latest data to some skeptical listeners, he concluded with: "I know there are people who can't believe all this—and why not? Then why don't you start making observations for forty years, because you need about forty years to separate the two orbits [of] twelve and twenty years. If this is real though, we have a situation similar to the Jupiter and Saturn situation [in our own solar system]. We find this because Barnard's Star was close enough [to us], and because it pleased Barnard's Star to be a single star with planets."

In Van de Kamp's last article on the subject before retiring to the Netherlands, where he resided until his death in May 1995, he summarized his analysis of more than four thousand photographic plates taken over the decades at the Sproul Observatory. In the article, Van de Kamp swore by his data, and expressed adamantly his belief that Barnard's Star is home to planets much like Jupiter and Saturn. "He never did see how he could possibly be wrong with all that large amount of data," says Gatewood. "He was sure the perturbation was going to occur again, and that we would all be reenlightened by its reoccurrence." Unfortunately, it has yet to do so.

Over the years, astronomers have taken thousands of photos, and have presented hundreds of papers, discussions, arguments, and mathematical analyses, all in an attempt to resolve the question: Does Barnard's Star have planets or not? They have made this rather obscure star barely 6 light-years away and buried from view among the star clouds of the Milky Way the focus of one of the longest and most conflicting studies in modern scientific history.

Van de Kamp did not stop with the planets of Barnard's Star, for he believed that this was just "the first tip—or tips—of the iceberg." He wrote: "How many planetary systems may be ready for discovery, and patiently await astrometric studies, by conventional photographic or other techniques? We shall always be confronted with threshold limitations—a natural condition of research, and very much so of the present long-focus photographic astrometric approach. But should we not come to the rescue of a cosmic phenomenon which may be trying to reveal itself in a sea of errors?"

For now, the planets of Barnard's Star remain unseen—if they exist at all. Decades' more study are still required to observe the star's motion and detect any minute wobblings that may be caused by an orbiting planetary system. Perhaps, in time, astronomers may show that Van de Kamp was right after all; that planets do exist around the star; perhaps around other stars as well.

Either way, discovering them will not be easy, for the detection of extrasolar planets has turned out to be a far more challenging technological effort than anyone had ever imagined. Such discoveries are now up to a new generation of astronomers, one which is armed with a revolutionary new arsenal of optics and electronic detectors.

3

It stands so tall that one can see it from Tucson, 90 kilometers to the east. White against the golden Arizona sunset, the giant dome of the 4-meter Mayall reflector telescope catches the eye of all who gaze westward. From the mountaintop site of the Kitt Peak National Observatory, the dome is an even more imposing structure, towering eighteen stories above surrounding landscape. Inside, the finest in optics is coupled with the latest in electronic detectors and computers to create one of the largest and most powerful telescopes in the world. This optical giant is in such demand that scientists often book it months in advance, mostly to seek and study the faintest and farthest galaxies and quasars in the universe. But, on a cool May night in 1984, astronomers were preparing the telescope for something totally different; they were planning to look at nearby stars in search of dark companion objects in orbit around them.

Astronomers Donald W. McCarthy, Jr., and Frank Low, of the University of Arizona, and Ronald Probst, of the National Optical Astronomy Observatories, were familiar with the search for extrasolar planets and, while they realized that such "discoveries" had proved false in the past, they had little doubt that planetary systems must exist out there—somewhere. The trick, they suspected, was finding the correct technique to reveal them. It wasn't long before they hit upon *speckle interferometry,* developed, in part, by the French astronomer Antoine Labeyrie in 1970. Its purpose was simple—to reduce significantly the blurring effects of the turbulent atmosphere and to produce sharper images at the focus of a telescope.

Anyone who has ever gazed into a starry sky knows this blurring effect well. Astronomers call it scintillation, but most everyone else knows it as twinkling. The effect is similar to that seen when viewing a distant landscape over a hot campfire or a car hood on a summer day. Hot air rises from the surface and bends the incoming light in different directions, creating a wobbly, wavering image. Seeing starlight is quite beautiful, but it is devastating to astronomers in search of fine detail. Even on a night when stars appear to shine steadily, starlight experiences continuous erratic movements in its image position and, on long exposure telescopic photographs, appears as blobs of light enlarged ten to fifty times.

To address this problem, astronomers developed the "speckle" technique. By taking a number of short exposures of a star in succession—each only 10 to 20 milliseconds in duration—they can freeze the effects of atmospheric turbulence so that each individual "speckle" in the overall image is distortion free. In other words, each stellar image is as perfect an image as one might see from a telescope orbiting high above the Earth's atmosphere. Large stars appear large, small stars appear small, and binary stars often show two distinct stars. Within each image lies remarkably fine detail that can be extracted by sophisticated statistical analysis—perhaps even clues to the existence of planetary companions that may otherwise remain undetected.

Even with this technique the trick to finding planets in orbit about distant stars seemed to be using it not with visible light, but rather with infrared radiation (IR). Compared with visible light, which radiates with waves of about 10^{-7} (0.0000001) meters in length, infrared is quite long, with wavelengths of around

10^{-6} (0.000001) to 10^{-4} (0.0001) meters. Since IR is nothing more than heat, everything in the universe from the hottest of stars to the coldest of ice—emits it unless the object should exist at the theoretical temperature of absolute zero (-273.14°C). In searching for planetary companions to other stars, McCarthy, Low, and Probst reasoned, infrared might prove extremely useful since these bodies would receive light from their parent stars, absorb it, and reradiate it in the form of IR, which could then be detected with specially designed telescopes.

Still, one might easily assume that the heat of the parent star would greatly overwhelm that of the planet itself. As it turns out, the answer is yes . . . and no. In visible light, stars like the sun shine by as much as 1 billion times more brightly than even Jupiter-like planets that may lie nearby. They would, presumably, drown out any planetary light by their intense glare and make it impossible to detect. In infrared, however, planets emit more radiation than in the visible spectrum, while most stars emit far less. While a planet's infrared emission would still pale in comparison to that of a star, the contrast between the two would be reduced by as much as ten times, providing astronomers a far greater chance of finding them.

These ideas produced exciting discussions during the early 1980s, but the technology required to create a two-dimensional infrared image with the resolution necessary to discover dark stellar companions was not available. So, instead of using a two-dimensional array in which an image could be taken directly, McCarthy and Low developed a one-dimensional adaptation for use with infrared. In this technique, a mirror rapidly swept a target star's image over a slit, a detector which measured the amount of infrared radiation coming from each point in the object. The researchers then scanned the star at right angles to the first, again measuring the "profile" of IR coming from the target along this direction. In this way they could mathematically "see" fine detail within the object without a single image ever being taken.

SERENDIPITY AT WORK

As is often the case in science, the idea for this new technique originated quite by accident several years earlier. While using the same 4-meter telescope on Kitt Peak to learn if certain star-forming regions of space were producing individual stars or clusters of stars, Donald McCarthy noticed something unusual when calibrating his detector. "I happened to point the telescope at what I thought was a double star named Zeta Aquarii," he recalled, "and got a very unusual response out of my instrument." He found not just two stars there, but a third as well.

What McCarthy didn't know at the time was that researchers at the U.S. Naval Observatory had only recently used long-term astrometric observations of Zeta Aquarii to predict the existence of a third body within the system—one with a mass about one-fourth that the sun. Apparently, it was this low-mass companion upon which McCarthy had stumbled.

After analyzing his data, and calculating the brightness and separation of the third component, McCarthy made a startling realization: "I discovered that, instead of using forty years of astrometric data, which can measure only the motion of the center of light of the system itself, we could suddenly, with one real measurement of angular separation, determine the individual masses of all the objects in the system. I thought that was a pretty powerful game and, in reading the literature, I started to realize that there were thirty-six astrometric binaries known—some of which were thought to have planetary companions. Although these should be too faint and we shouldn't be able to see them, it was definitely worth searching."

McCarthy began scouring the list of possible candidate stars on which to try his new technique. He found that, in systems where a companion larger than about 0.08 solar masses was predicted, he was able to spot it easily but, in cases like Barnard's Star, where only Jupiter-sized objects were suspected, he found nothing.

The limitations, it seemed, were determined by the brightness difference between the primary star and its darker companion, and McCarthy's team soon realized that if a star outshone its darker companion by more than 100 to 1, a search for the companion would be fruitless. On the other hand, if they could focus their effort on tiny, faint red dwarf stars, where the brightness ratios should be much less, they might have more luck. It was with this strategy that the Arizona astronomers began a longer, more comprehensive search for whatever bodies were lurking in the vicinity of nearby stars. "It just seemed like a happy hunting ground that no one else had the capability of touching," McCarthy recalls.

It wasn't long before the researchers went down the list of astrometric binaries and, with very few exceptions, found the predicted companions. Most were stars of low mass too faint to be seen by conventional methods from Earth. One object, however, in orbit about a faint star in the summertime constellation Ophiuchus, immediately caught their attention. The star was Van Biesbroeck 8 (VB8), named for the Belgian-American astronomer George Van Biesbroeck, who developed special techniques to discover intrinsically faint stars.

Ironically, when McCarthy began his observing project, VB8 was not known as an astrometric binary; he chose it simply because it was one of the lowest luminosity stars in the heavens. It was not until the autumn of 1984 that USNO astronomer Robert Harrington published a paper based on astrometric data that suggested that the star had a companion object nearby. By then, however, McCarthy's group had gathered their own data. "Our first results came from the four-meter telescope," he explained, "and seemed to show that there was [indeed, a companion] there." To be certain their data were not being influenced by some terrestrial or optical effect, he repeated the observations on several nights, at two different infrared wavelengths, and with two separate telescopes. Still, the results remained: VB8 appeared to have a previously unseen companion in orbit around it.

That McCarthy saw anything at all was amazing. "It's a difficult observation to make because VB8 happens to be one of the faintest things we've ever looked at, and it's difficult to do in the summer, given Tucson's cloudy weather." If that weren't enough, VB8 lay at a distance of 21 light-years from Earth, and its companion object—now designated VB8-B—appeared barely 1 arc second from its parent star (about the separation of two automobile headlights as viewed from a distance of 200 kilometers) and shone forty times fainter than its parent star.

What it was, no one knew. But it did not take astronomers long to recognize the importance of the discovery for, if it proved to be real, it represented the first direct detection of a previously unseen companion, and might enable astronomers to understand these objects as never before. "In the past, we had wobbling measurements that indicated the presence of a companion," explains McCarthy. "These tell you virtually nothing about it. But once you can directly detect the light, then you can [study] the physical characteristics of such objects—temperature, luminosity, diameter, chemical composition—all the normal things you can [study] with stars. Having that ability is what made this a breakthrough."

From the faint flickers of light received from VB8-B, the astronomers deduced the physical nature of the body. "We guessed that it would have about the same size as Jupiter, but maybe ten to thirty times more mass, and a temperature of about eleven hundred degrees Celsius," recalls McCarthy. "Otherwise, we expected it to be very similar to Jupiter—the same gaseous composition without a rocky surface to stand on. And it was revolving around a red dwarf star every few decades at about the same distance as Jupiter is from our sun."

As dramatic a discovery as this seemed to be, McCarthy, Low, and Probst were concerned with checking and rechecking their results before making an announcement. "My motivation was to be cautious and conservative about this because we were now potentially talking about [the discovery of] a planet. We spent a lot of time thinking about it and trying to interpret our results. We wrote a paper and submitted it. We didn't say anything about the results at the time, although we were preparing a press release. I worked with the National Science Foundation (the project's funding source) in writing the release, trying to get it exactly right with words like 'could be' and 'needs to be confirmed.' It never occurred to me that they might put a title on it." The title they selected was "Astronomers Discover First Planet Outside Solar System."

WHAT A REACTION!

The public's response was immediate and overwhelming. "I was really unprepared for what the word 'planet' conveys, and for the reaction of the world. People just descended. *Good Morning America* and the CBS *Morning News* came out to Kitt Peak. Frank Low and I drove up there on a foggy, windy, and icy morning to do the shows at six A.M. I remember doing this live interview—having an earphone on and having some guy in New York ask me questions that I wasn't at all prepared to answer. We had to have the four-meter telescope moving in the background. It was really wild."

Once the story hit the press, newspaper and magazine articles began accumulating on McCarthy's shelves. Then the letters started pouring in. "I got one—a certified letter that I had to drive to the post office to get—from a gal who was basically an astrologer. She had predicted that a tenth planet would someday be discovered in our solar system and, of course, that's what she thought our object was. She had taken out this copyright agreement on a name, so she felt she had all the right to name the damned thing. VB8-B just wouldn't do!" Another came from a man who published his own newsletter on archaeology and anthropology. "He claimed that there was some ten-thousand-year-old pebble he had found with an inscription on it that he could never decipher. Now he realized that it was the constellation of Ophiuchus where VB8 is, and that basically VB8-B must have been discovered ten thousand years ago!"

Perhaps even more surprising to McCarthy, Low, and Probst

was another group that quickly pounced. These were the astronomers, some of whom were upset that the newly found object was being referred to as a planet. "It had never occurred to me that you couldn't call this thing a planet," explains McCarthy. "It was an object that's not massive enough to generate energy by nuclear fusion, and it's revolving around a star. It's just a large Jupiter, guys! But that's not what everyone thought. I quickly found out that there were a wide variety of definitions of the word 'planet' floating around among astronomers."

Soon, astronomers around the country were calling the media to dispute the issue. First, the U.S. Naval Observatory made the claim that they should be considered the discoverers of VB8-B. "Clearly they published a paper with astrometric data that showed a companion," says McCarthy, "and somehow they felt we weren't giving them enough credit. So they had their own news conference to sort of contest ours. They wanted to stake their claim that they had been there first. Then Ron Probst's old thesis adviser—a guy named Kumar at the University of Virginia—decided to hold his own news conference. He wanted to let the press know that he thought this all was a bunch of rubbish, and that Ron should know better than to call such a thing a planet."

With each succeeding news conference, the press descended on Tucson for the Arizona astronomers' reaction. "We went through wave after wave of this stuff. The excitement wore out real fast, and I was really getting tired of it. I shot about a year working on the public opinion of this, but I answered every single one of the inquiries. It was just incredible!"

PLANET OR STAR?

The body they called VB8-B sparked the imagination of the general public, yet, to astronomers, it represented more than just a fascinating discovery. It challenged what many believed was a fundamental distinction in astronomy—the difference between stars and planets. Here was an object that appeared far hotter and more massive than any planet ever found, yet seemed much too small and cool to shine on its own and be considered a full-fledged star. So was it a star or a planet? Even the best scientific minds were puzzled.

The problem is that no clear distinction between stars and planets had ever been devised. There are, of course, common ways of distinguishing the two in the sky. Planets generally don't twinkle; stars do. Planets reflect light; stars shine on their own. Planets move among the stars; stars are fixed. Planets appear disklike through telescopes; stars do not. By these criteria, VB8-B—if located in the solar system—might look remarkably similar to Jupiter. Astronomers would then call it a planet as it wandered through the sky from year to year. But the issue was more than just one of semantics. It was one of physics. What makes a planet a planet? What makes a star a star? Are the two interchangeable? Can a planet become a star, or a star a planet? And what is the physical difference between the two?

Even a cursory look around the universe shows that stars are tremendously hot globes of gas that shine on their own, while planets are relatively cool solid or gaseous bodies that orbit a star and merely reflect its light. The difference is much like that between a light bulb that is turned off versus one that is turned on. One shines on its own, while the other reflects the light of other glowing bulbs, yet both are considered light bulbs. Is it possible, then, that planets and stars are simply manifestations of the same natural phenomenon—that one is merely hot enough to emit radiation on its own, while the other is not?

This "planetary rule of thumb" seems to work well until one looks closely at a world like Jupiter. Here is a body that emits nearly one and a half times more radiation than it receives from the sun—mostly in the form of infrared and radio waves not visible to the human eye. Yet, if the eyes were sensitive to these emissions, Jupiter would appear quite luminous in the sky. Would astronomers then consider it a star? Is it only called a planetary body because it does not radiate in the spectral band that humans can perceive? If so, then the distinction between stars and planets depends entirely on perception, rather than on physical reality—a situation scientists prefer to avoid.

So what is it that determines whether an object shines by visible light or by reflected light? Its mass. Stars are composed mostly of hydrogen gas and, in order to convert hydrogen to helium within its core, a star must achieve a certain combination of internal temperature and pressure. The greater a body's mass happens to be, the greater the pressure and temperature it experiences at its core. If a body contains enough mass—more than about eighty times that of Jupiter—the temperature at its core will soar to more than 10 million degrees. At this temperature, hydrogen atoms race about with such force that they slam into one another and fuse, creating helium and releasing tremendous amounts of energy. Ultimately this energy radiates outward into space and the body shines on its own. This would then be easily considered a star.

A continuum of masses exists from the smallest to the largest of stars. A similar continuum exists for smaller bodies within the solar system—from the tiniest of dust specks to the largest planets. In between the realm of the stars and the realm of the planets, however, exists a gap that has always served as a natural dividing line between planets and stars. Bodies on the large side of this boundary had always been considered stars; those on the small side, planets.

But suppose a body contains just enough mass to place it squarely within this gap—say about seventy times that of Jupiter. Its internal temperature would still be quite high, but not high enough to spark hydrogen fusion. The body would, instead, glow only in the infrared (heat) and, if it were near enough to Earth, a human would see it only by the light it reflects from a "real" star. It might, then, appear as a planet. It was just such a phenomenon that astronomers were facing in VB8-B.

Clearly, a fundamental problem exists in defining the distinction between stars and planets—one that goes far beyond semantics, and one that results in a fascinating catch-22 situation. How can astronomers ever hope to distinguish between stars and planets unless they find other planetary examples to compare? And how can astronomers ever find such planetary examples until they can distinguish between planets and stars?

In trying to understand the physical relationship between the two phenomena, some have suggested that a star might be defined as any body that shines by hydrogen fusion. On the surface it seems like a good idea, but even this isn't foolproof. White dwarfs, for example, are old stars near the end of their lives. They have recently blasted away their atmospheres and have collapsed to become hot, dense stars the size of Earth with virtually no hydrogen remaining in their cores. Their glow originates from the heat generated by their gravitational collapse into their present state, not from the fusion of hydrogen, yet astronomers see them in visible light and call them stars. Still other objects become hot enough to burn deuterium (heavy hydrogen) but not "regular" hydrogen. Should these be called stars even though deuterium burning produces no visible light at all?

The actual dividing line between stars and planets, if one even exists, is anyone's guess, and that is the reason the announcement of VB8-B created such shock waves throughout the astronomical community. Whatever it was, the body seemed to fall squarely in the gap between what was known as stars and what was known as planets. It was unlike any star ever seen, yet unlike any planet in the solar system and, for lack of a better description, scientists classified it as a "substellar" object—a peculiar missing link between stars and planets. It seemed to suggest that a smooth continuum of sizes and masses might just exist from the smallest of planets to the largest of stars.

LILLIPUTIAN STARS AND BROBDINGNAGIAN PLANETS

As unusual an object as VB8-B seemed, it was not the first time that anyone had ever thought about such a body. It was the American astronomer Harlow Shapley who first suggested the existence of substellar objects in the late 1950s. He described an entire continuum of objects from the largest of stars to the smallest of planets and, in the gap between the two, objects not at all unlike VB8-B. "They would have mass enough to contract into stable permanent bodies with a dense atmosphere," he wrote, "but not mass enough to shine so effectively that they could be seen unless very near. The whole range of sizes, from those of 1/50 the solar mass, which one might call dark Lilliputian stars, to those 1/500 the mass of the sun, which might be called Brobdingnagian planets, could be represented by countless sidereal bodies. They may be more numerous than the recognized stars."

In describing these bodies, Shapley also recognized the problems scientists might face in searching for them. "The largest of the Lilliputians would shine faintly in infrared light, and could be detected if near at hand, but mostly they are lightless wanderers. Eventually, scientific techniques may enable astronomers to detect them."

Imagining these strange objects and understanding their physical nature, though, were two completely different matters. It wasn't until the early 1960s that scientists began to probe the theoretical differences between stellar and substellar objects. A normal star, they knew, stopped collapsing from its embryonic cloud when hydrogen fusion kicked in, establishing and supporting the new star. Substellar objects, on the other hand, were not massive enough for hydrogen fusion to begin so their collapse would stop only when they reached a point called "electron degeneracy"—when all the matter in the body's core is compressed to such a degree that the negatively charged electrons are crammed up against one another. Only then would the repulsion of like charges prevent the star from collapsing further. Unlike normal stars, these substellar objects could never become hot enough to ignite hydrogen fusion and would just continue to radiate into space the heat produced by their gravitational collapse until, someday, they simply ran out of energy and vanished.

In the mid-1970s, Jill Tarter, a young graduate student at the University of California at Berkeley, began developing some

mathematical models to help explain both the physics of substellar objects and the number that might actually exist. While
Tarter recognized how difficult such objects would be to find,
she suggested how they might appear to Earth-bound and space-
borne telescopes. When she came to the question of a name,
however, a problem of terms arose. In order to communicate
the uncertainty of her models, as well as the ruddy glow that
these small objects might emit, she suggested the term "brown
dwarf."

Of course, no brown dwarfs had ever been found, and no one
realistically expected that they might be anytime soon, leaving
theoreticians to turn their attentions toward more pressing astrophysical problems. The idea of the brown dwarf became rel-
egated to one of a mere curiosity. When McCarthy's team
announced its discovery of VB8-B in 1984, however, theoreticians sat up and took notice and their interest in brown dwarfs
was rekindled. Here, at last, was an object that seemed, in all
respects, to fit the bill of a substellar object. Perhaps it was a
planet or perhaps it was a brown dwarf but either way, it represented the first such discovery. It held the promise of becoming a valuable observational test of what had long been just an
interesting theory.

Theoreticians began riffling through their files for their old
work on brown dwarfs but soon realized that their understanding of stars and planets had evolved considerably since the first
research was done. Two decades earlier, when thinking began
in earnest about the origin of the solar system, most scientists
assumed that planets formed in much the same way as stars.
Instead of forming a multiple or binary star system, they believed, fragments of a collapsing cloud of gas and dust would
spin off and condense to form planets. But now, with spacecraft
data from nearly all of the Earth's planetary neighbors in hand,
planetary scientists could evaluate their old theories a bit more
objectively.

If planets formed in the same manner as stars, they reasoned,
then the chemical compositions of both Jupiter and Saturn

should appear identical to that of the sun. They do not. The *Voyager* spacecraft, which flew by these worlds in the late 1970s and early 1980s, measured their gravitational fields and revealed that they have, instead, cores of heavy elements—carbon, nitrogen, oxygen—which are surrounded by huge gaseous atmospheres of hydrogen and helium. This means that Jupiter and Saturn cannot be simple condensations of gas like the sun. The only plausible way such a planet could exist is by first forming a solid core of rock and ice that eventually becomes large enough to attract gas from the nearby protoplanetary disk into a thick gaseous atmosphere.

Whatever VB8-B was, it certainly didn't appear to fit this model of planetary formation. The data suggested, instead, that it must have condensed directly from the interstellar material into a spherical, gaseous object. While it seemed much the same size as the planet Jupiter, there seemed to be a fundamental difference in the genesis of these two bodies.

Armed with their new knowledge of planetary and stellar evolution, theoreticians began to explore in detail how objects like VB8-B might form, and found only three possible outcomes of the starbirth process. In one model, clouds of interstellar gas and dust collapse to form single stars with no companions. This scenario seems to be quite rare, at least in this part of the galaxy. Another possible outcome is a star surrounded by a disk. If a newly formed star spins rapidly, stellar material might be thrown outward creating a thin disk where rocky and gassy worlds could form. But bodies larger than ten or twenty times more massive than Jupiter could never form here, simply because the material in a disk would become exhausted long before an object of such mass could coalesce.

The most propitious scenario, then, for the formation of substellar objects is that in which a star is formed with one or more companion stars—a binary or multiple star system. Such systems appear to be quite common in the Milky Way galaxy. Suppose a newborn star leaves behind enough excess material to form a companion object, but one not larger than 80 Jupiter masses.

The resulting substellar object would become very hot, but not hot enough to fuse hydrogen in its core and radiate visible light. It would be, essentially, a stillborn star. It was through this third model of starbirth that theoreticians hoped to explain the existence of an object like VB8-B.

MAKING A BROWN DWARF

A brown dwarf, it is now believed, begins its life much like any star—from a huge molecular cloud somewhere in the galaxy. As material clumps together, some fragments become denser than others, attracting more and more gas in a "snowball" effect. Eventually, the gas fragments collapse upon themselves, converting their potential energy into heat as they fall inward toward the center of the growing body. Ultimately, each collapsing body becomes so compact that it is no longer just a collection of gas fragments, but a spherical, self-luminous object as bright as a star.

In a body heavier than about 80 Jupiter masses, nuclear fusion would begin at this point, providing an opposite force to halt further collapse. In a smaller body—one between 20 and 80 Jupiter masses—fusion never begins, however, and the material continues to fall in upon itself until electron degeneracy halts the collapse. With no energy being produced in its core, the brown dwarf begins to cool. Its internal heat, built up from its long, slow collapse, is now passed outward through the body's interior and radiated into space. The rate at which it cools, however, depends on its size. The smaller the object, the smaller will be its surface area and, therefore, the slower the body will cool.

After some 10 million years, the brown dwarf will have cooled to a point where it shines a thousand times fainter than the sun. Now, everything that happens to it occurs at and above its atmosphere, while its internal structure changes very little. Grains of dust begin to form—analogous to clouds on Earth—and loose elements combine into molecules and block the escape of heat. By the age of 100 million years, the brown dwarf glows only ten thousand times fainter than the sun. After a billion years have passed, its atmosphere will have cooled to a mere 2,800 degrees Celsius, barely half the temperature of the sun, and would contain mostly molecular gas.

If the life of a brown dwarf could be projected even farther, say beyond 10 billion years and the life of the entire universe, one would find that the dust grains would form deeper within its atmosphere, and molecules more typical of colder objects, such as methane, would form. When the temperature dropped to about minus 200 to minus 100 degrees Celsius, water clouds would begin to form and, eventually, even molecular hydrogen would condense.

Brown dwarfs now intrigue astronomers because they might help answer some of their most fundamental questions about the universe. For example, studies of the Milky Way and other galaxies tend to suggest that they contain considerably more mass than is accounted for by the combined mass of luminous stars—perhaps as much as 90 percent of the mass of the universe. If this is true, then perhaps the combined gravitational force of all this dark matter may one day cause the universe to collapse back upon itself into an ultradense state similar to that which most astronomers now believe caused the big bang itself. It is possible that brown dwarfs might account for this "missing mass"—a huge population of hard-to-see objects in the void between the stars.

Astronomers also see in brown dwarfs a chance to gain a greater understanding of how stars form and how they work. Within the Milky Way galaxy alone, hundreds of billions of stars shine and, through the studies of their spectra, astronomers can learn the chemistry and physics of nuclear fusion, how energy is transported from the core into a star's atmosphere, and how intense magnetic fields interact with charged materials. But how do gaseous globes behave when hydrogen fusion does *not* begin? Brown dwarfs may provide a laboratory in which that question can finally be answered.

Perhaps an even more profound question arises for which

brown dwarfs may provide the answer: Do planetary systems exist out there among the stars? By understanding how frequently stars form with a brown dwarf companion, one might, in turn, learn how frequently disks and planetary systems can form. Most astronomers now believe that a fair number of brown dwarfs should exist in the Milky Way—perhaps not enough to account for the missing mass of the universe, but a respectable number when compared to the luminous stars. Given that this galaxy is at least 10 billion years old, most of the brown dwarfs must also be fairly old and, therefore, quite faint.

Against this background it is easy to understand why the announcement of VB8-B created such a stir. Here at last, it seemed, was an object that fit the description of a brown dwarf—a laboratory in which theoreticians could test their mathematical models. But one important characteristic was missing: its mass. Since a brown dwarf's mass determines its internal temperature (and hence its size and cooling rate), the problem might be solved backward. If astronomers could determine its age, they could then use its fading luminosity to calculate its mass.

The star VB8 (and its apparent companion VB8-B) appears to be part of a small star cluster known as Wolf 630. Since all stars in the cluster were presumably born together from the same collapsing gas cloud, learning the age of one was as simple as learning the age of the group. However, astronomers soon found that some of its stars showed unmistakable signs of youth, while others appeared quite old. How old VB8 (and more importantly, VB8-B) might be was now anyone's guess.

"It could be the age of our solar system, or it could be ten times younger," said McCarthy. "Its age actually makes me a bit uncomfortable because these things are supposed to cool off with time." The problem arose when comparing the object's observed brightness and temperature with predictions based on theoretical cooling rates. One possibility was that VB8-B was still a relatively young object in its rapid cooling phase—only about 500 million years old and with a mass somewhat less than 50 Jupiters. If it were older than this, say a billion years or more, scientists would need to explain why its brightness did not match up with mathematical predictions. "If it really is that old and bright," McCarthy mused, "it may mean that our theories of such things are out the window."

SEARCHING FOR ANSWERS

During the next few years, VB8-B began to experience the same problem as Barnard's Star two decades earlier. Several independent teams of astronomers from both Europe and the United States aimed telescopes toward VB8-B with hopes of seeing the object and determining its age. But no one could find a trace of the body. McCarthy himself also went back to the telescope to take another look. Despite a painstakingly careful search, he couldn't find it either. "We tried to keep observing it," he recalls, "but the equipment never worked as well. We didn't have the sensitivity or we didn't have the [lack of turbulence in the atmosphere]. We just never had the same opportunity."

Large bodies like this don't just disappear so astronomers offer some more rational explanations. One is that the object may have dimmed over the ensuing years. A decrease in brightness of at least sixteen times would be necessary to account for its disappearance—a phenomenon most astronomers consider unlikely for a brown dwarf. Another possibility is that VB8-B may have become lost in the glare of its parent star—an effect that could occur if it orbits in a highly elongated path. If so, then VB8-B should pop back into view on the other side in just a few years. "I guess you really have to appeal to variability," says McCarthy, "[but I] don't think there's any reasonable orbit that would cause it to disappear for so long." Certainly the astrometric evidence for this companion to VB8 should help solve the mystery, but it seems to have "disappeared" as well. Not only have new observations since VB8-B's "discovery" failed to reveal the low-mass companion, new measurements of older photographic plates have turned up empty as well.

Whatever could have happened to VB8-B? One of the most

popular theories currently is that the body never existed in the first place—that the original observations somehow fell victim to the Earth's wavering and unpredictable atmosphere, or to the very observational technique that astronomers used to find it. "[VB8-B] was one of the faintest and most difficult things we've ever looked at," recalls McCarthy. "Whenever you reach those limits of your detector or your technique, you have to be really careful. So I think that, even today, we're all basically in disbelief that it could be explained so easily by an atmospheric [effect], and we keep pondering new ways to look at VB8-B."

Despite his philosophical outlook, McCarthy remains disappointed. "It was disappointing not so much that we couldn't lay claim to being the first," says McCarthy, "but that maybe we had misled people. Back a few years ago, entire conferences and National Science Foundation proposals were being based on VB8-B. There was a conference at George Mason University on Brown dwarfs motivated completely by this result. In the end, that's one of the good things that came of VB8-B—that it generated an awful lot of thinking on what objects like this should look like. And that's not lost; that's valuable to have."

In the meantime, all scientists could do is continue searching. Historically, discovery often comes in starts and stops, with unusual types of objects tentatively identified and then retracted. Often this comes from pushing technology to its limits. Eventually, however, technology becomes good enough to confirm the existence of previously unseen objects. Such may ultimately prove true with brown dwarfs. If it does, their properties will most likely challenge the theoreticians and help sharpen their mathematical models. If brown dwarfs turn out to be extremely rare, then astronomers will have learned something important as well.

Just as with Barnard's Star two decades earlier, the search was reduced from the realm of the observational to the theoretical. Dark companions were proved once again to be far more elusive than anyone could have imagined and astronomers were forced to take a step back to answer a fundamental question: What exactly are we seeking?

4

S Y S T E M S   L I K E   O U R S

Twice the discovery of planets in orbit around other stars has been exuberantly announced, only to have it turn out that the "planets" were most likely illusions—products of the technology used to seek them out. As a result of these two events, astronomers were forced to look very hard at their methods of planetary detection, and to ask themselves some very difficult and fundamental questions. For example: What are we looking for in an extrasolar planet? Are we searching in the right places with the right techniques? Is our understanding of the nature of planets and stars even correct? Obviously, planets can exist—at least around the star known as the sun. To determine if this planetary system is or is not unique, astronomers must first determine *how* it formed and whether that process is unusual or common.

Even a cursory glance around the Solar System reveals the diverse forms that planets can take. They range from heat-seared and blistered Mercury, only 58 million kilometers from the sun, to the cosmic deep freeze of Neptune and Pluto billions of kilometers away. In between lie worlds of remarkable beauty and variety: from the colossal cloudscapes of Jupiter to the glorious rings of Saturn; from the Martian polar ice caps to the tropical rain forests of Earth.

At first it might seem that the variety of worlds of the sun's planetary family couldn't possibly be related—that this star somehow swept together nine cosmic rogues into a makeshift family. "Catastrophic" theories such as this were common centuries ago, when astronomers were first struggling to explain the existence of this seemingly odd collection of worlds. Catastrophists invoked rare accidents, sudden events, unusual circumstances—even the intervention of a creator—to make sense out of an otherwise puzzling situation.

Perhaps the first to suggest that the planets of the Solar System were the result of some bizarre cosmic accident was the eighteenth-century French naturalist Georges-Louis Leclerc, Comte de Buffon. In 1745, Leclerc suggested that the sun had long ago collided with an immense body, perhaps a wandering comet, causing a violent eruption of gas. Since this gas would not have quite enough energy to escape the gravitational pull of the sun, it fell neatly into orbit around it, eventually cooling and condensing into the planets of today. Others modified this idea slightly, and suggested that the impact was not direct, but that the sun might have been only sideswiped by a "hit and run" star. This near collision tore from the sun a cigar-shaped gaseous filament that ultimately gave birth to the planets. Its thicker mid-section condensed into the gas giant planets, while the smaller planets, asteroids, moons, and comets formed from its thinner and smaller ends.

It did not take long, however, for astronomers to recognize major contradictions within these scenarios. For one, hot gas torn or ejected from the sun could never have condensed into planetary bodies but, instead, would have fallen back into the sun or dispersed into space. Neither of these eventualities would lead to the formation of planets. Further, stars in the sun's neighborhood of the galaxy are so tremendously far apart that they seldom, if ever, collide. For example, if stars could be reduced from million-kilometer-diameter glowing spheres to the size of garden peas, only three would fit into the state of Arizona and *these* would be moving in random directions at a "breakneck" speed of one city block per year. Under these circumstances, the odds of a collision—or even a near collision—occurring between stars would be one in many millions.

It seems terribly unlikely that this planetary system could have originated in this catastrophic way. If it did, it might be the only one in existence and that would be the end of the story, but scientists dislike complex theories that require unusual physical processes that may occur only once in the history of the universe. The whole of modern scientific method is based on a principle known as Occam's razor, named for William of Occam, the fourteenth-century British philosopher who first proposed it. It states that the simplest of available hypotheses best explains an unexplained phenomenon.

Catastrophic theories of planetary formation are far from simple. They require an unusual cosmic encounter to tear off material from the sun and virtually impossible physical processes to force swirling hot gasses to condense into cooler solid bodies. If astronomers were to learn the true nature of the Solar System, how it originated and how it might compare to others that might exist, they would require a totally different approach—one that relied upon less fantastic physical occurrences.

What was necessary, according to David Black, a planetary scientist with the Lunar and Planetary Institute in Houston, and one of the key players in deciphering the workings of the sun's planetary family, was to "defocus"—to concentrate not on the fine details of *this* system, but to identify what might be gross attributes of planetary systems in general. In this way scientists hope to make general predictions about what they might find elsewhere. In principle, the approach is straightforward. All one would need to do is to view the sun's planetary family not as a collection of random and disordered worlds, but rather as a *system* of worlds. When this is done, some fascinating patterns begin to emerge.

*　*　*

DISCOVERING THE SYSTEM

Viewed from above, the Solar System would appear as a flattened disk, with the sun at the center and nine planets and countless asteroids and comets circling it. But, because Pluto does not fit the patterns displayed by all the other planets, some debate its classification as a "planet." For example, all the planetary bodies appear to be about the same age and to orbit the sun counterclockwise in nearly circular orbits—except for Pluto, whose orbit is highly elliptical. Also, nearly all spin in the plane and direction of their orbital motion—the same plane and direction in which the sun itself is turning—except Pluto, whose orbit is tipped about 17 degrees to plane of the Solar System.

These planetary orbits are spaced regularly throughout the disk—with each one nearly twice as far from the sun as the one preceding it—again, with the exception of Pluto, whose orbit occasionally takes it inside that of Neptune. Those planets farthest from the sun take the longest to orbit, partially because their orbits are larger and partially because the sun's gravitational force on them is weaker. Mercury, for example, whips around the sun in less than three Earth-months, while Neptune takes more than one and a half Earth-centuries to complete its journey.

The planetary bodies themselves display a striking pattern as well. Leaving enigmatic Pluto aside, the planets fall into three main groups. Those nearest the sun are small worlds composed mostly of rock and metal—the terrestrial planets, Mercury, Venus, Earth, and Mars—so named because they resemble the Earth in size, makeup, and mass. These solid worlds lie within some 230 million kilometers of the sun, and are essentially devoid of hydrogen and helium, the most abundant chemical elements in the universe. They rotate rather slowly on their axes with periods ranging from nearly twenty-four hours for the Earth to 245 Earth-days for Venus. Most are pocked with impact craters that date back millions or billions of years, and their atmospheres are relatively thin or—in the the case of Mercury—virtually nonexistent.

Beyond Mars, however, the planetary family appears radically different. Between 750 and 1,500 million kilometers from the sun lie the gas giants Jupiter and Saturn. These mammoth worlds are engulfed by bloated atmospheres of hydrogen, helium, methane, and ammonia, and spin so rapidly—once every ten Earth-hours or so—that they bulge at their equators. Buried deep within each may lie a core of ice and rock as much as twenty times more massive than the Earth itself.

Finally, in the outer reaches of the system—3 to 6 billion kilometers from the warmth of the sun—lie the icy twins Uranus and Neptune. These worlds, too, are surrounded by thick atmospheres but have very little hydrogen and helium. They contain, instead, mostly ices of methane and ammonia that may surround an icy core deep within.

The number of moons orbiting the planets suggests an intriguing pattern as well. Among the four terrestrial worlds, only three moons exist—two orbiting Mars and one orbiting Earth. The situation is quite different for the outer planets, however, for here moons abound. Orbiting the planets Jupiter, Saturn, Uranus, and Neptune are more than four dozen moons, and all, except Neptune, have systems that orbit within the plane of their planet's equator. Perhaps most intriguing are the four largest moons of Jupiter—the Galilean satellites (so called because they were discovered by Galileo nearly four centuries ago)—which, from the dense moons closest to Jupiter to the lighter spheres of ice farther away, all orbit in the same plane and same direction thus forming a version of the solar system in microcosm.

The appearance of rings around some of the planets provides another interesting pattern. Only the four giant, gaseous worlds are encircled by rings—which range from the brilliant ring complex at Saturn to the broken twisted skeins around Neptune. While they appear solid, each ring is composed of thousands of ringlets containing billions of particles of water ice (or in the case of Jupiter, rocks) that whirl about their parent planets in individual orbits.

Separating the inner rocky planets from the outer gaseous worlds is a ring of asteroids: countless chunks of rock that range from the size of pebbles to that of large mountains, tumbling endlessly around the sun. Asteroids appear to be composed of a mixture of materials from the metal-rich inner system and the volatile-rich outer system, and seem to form a natural division between the two types of worlds.

Permeating the plane of the inner Solar System exists a vast cloud of dust, perhaps the litter of countless comets that have long since passed our way, or of tumbling asteroids that have slowly ground each other into rubble. Beyond, in the cold, dark reaches of the system, where even the brilliant sun would appear as but another star in a darkened sky, a swarm of comets is believed to orbit the sun in highly elongated and tipped paths. Like the surfaces of some outer planets' satellites, these cosmic snowballs are composed mostly of water ice, with trapped or frozen gases like carbon dioxide, silicate dust, and dark carbonaceous material within.

The Solar System is not just a collection of random and disordered bodies but exhibits instead a simple, yet remarkable, structure that most likely resulted from noncatastrophic processes. Today, astronomers believe that they can use these structural regularities to glean clues to the system's birth and evolution. Much as a detective can reconstruct the events of a crime from the evidence left behind, modern astronomers are using sophisticated theoretical calculations, photos and measurements by planetary probes, laboratory analyses of ancient meteorites, and telescopic studies of interstellar material to reconstruct the birth of the Solar System billions of years ago. While no single comprehensive theory yet exists to explain the wealth of planetary data gathered in recent years, astronomers have put forth several likely scenarios that may explain how the system came to be.

JOURNEYING BACK

To reconstruct the origin of this planetary system, astronomers have imagined what the environment must have been like some 5 billion years ago near the edge of the typical spiral galaxy now known as the Milky Way. It was in this place that a huge, slowly rotating cloud began to collapse—a cold, dark mass billions of kilometers across and composed mostly of hydrogen and helium, of tiny molecular grains scattered randomly throughout, and of traces of heavy elements blasted into space by exploding stars of ages past. For eons, the cloud had remained stable—its grains held together by their own gravitation that perfectly balanced their natural efforts to escape. Then, within a few million years, things began to change.

Inside the cloud, gravity overtook the particles' individual motions, and the nebula began to collapse. In some areas, where the particle density was greater than average, clumps formed and began to spin on their own as turbulent vortices—each hundreds or thousands of times more massive than the sun. Eventually, turbulence broke each vortex into hundreds or thousands of smaller spinning fragments that eventually became cloudy disks out of which new stars, and possibly new planetary systems, could one day be born. One of these became the sun and the solar system.

In this smaller primordial nebula, gravity continued to dominate. As it collapsed, the fragment spun more rapidly—much as an ice skater whirls faster as she pulls her outstretched arms inward. At the same time, centrifugal force threw the accompanying material outward into a thick, pancakelike disk. This disk was not solid and did not spin uniformly. Material near the center whirled about in only days, while that farther out took centuries to complete one orbit. Matter continued to fall inward while the disk's center grew to a bulge more than 30 million kilometers across. Increasing gravitational pressures slowed its collapse, and caused the temperature to soar to thousands of degrees. The "protosun" had been born.

Now, intense heat flowed outward from the newly formed protosun into the dark surrounding disk. Nearest the center, nearly all was vaporized; no ice, no water, no hydrogen, could possibly exist under those conditions. In fact, only the least volatile of rock and metallic materials could survive there. Farther out, however, conditions were different. Out beyond several hundred million kilometers from the protosun, temperatures plummeted to hundreds of degrees below zero, and solids found it easier to survive. Water froze easily within the shadows of dusty particles, and volatile gases such as hydrogen, helium, methane, and ammonia were plentiful. Near the outer edge of the disk hundreds of billions of kilometers away, temperatures hovered only a few degrees above absolute zero, and even the volatile gases such as methane and ammonia began to freeze.

Centuries passed, and temperatures throughout the disk continued to cool. Gases condensed and froze onto the surfaces of larger dust grains, much like frost on a cold winter night, forming "fluffy" particles nearly a centimeter across. On occasion, these newly formed "snowflakes" collided and stuck together to form even larger flakes which, in turn, attracted others more rapidly with their stronger gravitational pull. Just as a snowball rolling downhill accumulates snow, twigs, leaves, and stones, each new "planetesimal" began to sweep up all in its path. Within just a few million years—still a brief instant in cosmic time—each grew to more than a hundred kilometers across and showed no signs of slowing.

In the inner disk, dust of silicates and heavy metallic oxides were most prevalent and accumulated into the rocky planets now known as Mercury, Venus, Earth, and Mars. In the outer regions, since the chemical abundances were considerably different, the newly forming bodies accumulated as much as twenty times more ice and gas as those in the inner disk and began to form the immense atmospheres of the gaseous giant planets: Jupiter, Saturn, Uranus, and Neptune.

In between the inner and outer disks, temperatures became

just right for carbon- and water-rich minerals to accrete into a good-sized planet. Instead, something peculiar began to happen. Powerful gravitational tides from the giant planet Jupiter drew away most of these building materials, scrambled the orbits of the gathering planetesimals, and prevented them from coalescing into a full-sized body. Because of this disruption, thousands of planetesimals remained—the largest, now known as the asteroid Ceres, hardly grew larger across than the state of New York.

Surrounding the disk orbited billions of tiny frozen bodies too far apart to coalesce or to be captured by one of the newly forming worlds. Over time, their orbital paths became deflected by the gravitational pull of nearby stars and the newly formed planets, and they were launched outward toward their permanent homes in a swarm tens of billions of kilometers away. These were the nascent comets. Permeating the entire newborn system remained a disk of remnant primordial materials—the dusty afterbirth of the planetary family.

As the planets, comets, and asteroids took shape, the central mass continued to draw material inward from the nebula, becoming constantly larger and hotter. Now completely enshrouded by a thick cloud of opaque dust, temperatures within rose from a few thousand to several million degrees. Thermonuclear reactions began, and the sun was born. Thrown out of balance by its powerful new energy source, the newborn sun burst erratically into view. In only a few million years, intense blasts threw into space as much as half the sun's mass and blew away from the inner disk nearly every speck of dust not held down to a planet by gravity.

Several million years passed before the sun's outwardly flowing energy reached a balance with the inward pull of gravity, and the star settled down to a more peaceful life. When it did, four large cinders—the terrestrial planets—remained nearby. Farther from the center, in what was once the outer disk of the primordial nebula, existed the giant worlds whose huge gaseous envelopes remained untouched by the explosive nature of the newborn sun.

SOME FINISHING TOUCHES

The birth of the system was far from complete, though. The gravitational collapse of the newly formed terrestrial planets, combined with the decay of radioactive elements within, caused temperatures deep inside to rise. The worlds became molten spheres, hot enough to drive any accumulated atmosphere off into space again. Heavy metals sank to the center of each of these worlds and formed a dense core, while lighter silicate materials floated to the top. Within a million years or so, each planet's outer layers had cooled and a crust had formed.

While most of the tiny dust specks of the inner protoplanetary disk had been blasted away by the sun's ignition, many larger chunks—the size of boulders or mountains—continued to stalk the area. For the next 500 million years, they rained down upon the primordial planets, tearing open their newly formed surfaces. Volcanoes and fissures released lava from within and sculpted the new worlds' features, while volcanic gases, rich in carbon dioxide, water, nitrogen, ammonia, and hydrogen sulfide, poured through the crusts, creating new atmospheres around these worlds. The smaller bodies—like Mercury and the moon—possessed insufficient gravitational pull to retain these new atmospheres. Mars, too, lost its grip, but much more slowly. Only the largest of the inner planets, Venus and Earth, retained virtually all of their atmospheres while losing most of their lightest gases such as hydrogen and helium. With the new atmospheres came weather, and soon atmospheric forces such as wind and rain began to erode the cratered evidence of this turbulent geological era.

A billion years passed. Most of the large, asteroid-sized planetesimals that pummeled the newborn worlds had either crashed into the inner planets or succumbed to the gravitational pull of the outer solar system, where they would remain as asteroids, comets, or moons of the giant planets.

In addition to the planetesimals captured from the inner solar system, tremendous amounts of primordial material remained around these outer worlds. Some of this matter had formed into a swirling disk analogous to the one that once surrounded the protosun. Jupiter, for example, had grown to a diameter of nearly a million and a half kilometers. Its internal temperatures and pressures rose, heat began to flow into the disk, and chemical elements began to separate much as they did in the early Solar System. Nearest to the warm planet, only rocky and metallic elements survived, while, farther out, ice and other volatile materials began condensing. Eventually, Jupiter gave birth to a family of moons that mimicked in many ways the structure of the Solar System itself. Its four largest became two inner moons of denser rock and metal and two distant ones of ice.

It was from this extraplanetary debris that the moons of the other outer planets formed as well. Just as chunks of material from the primordial solar disk were deflected into elongated orbits as asteroids or comets, some of the newly formed satellites became similarly perturbed. Other satellites were captured as they wandered through the Solar System from interplanetary space, and were flung into the peripheries of the giant planet systems. In this newly forming system of bodies, gravitational tides disrupted the accretion in parts of the disk and scattered the debris into rings of ice and rock.

ARE WE CORRECT?

This is how astronomers now think the system began—as a natural by-product of the sun's birth. The theory just described meets the criteria of Occam's razor; that is, it does not rely on extraordinary events. This theory also fuels optimism that other planetary systems may have formed out there among the stars. "I think if you look at the way our perception of how the solar system is formed, there's gradually emerging a paradigm," says

David Black of the Lunar and Planetary Institute. "That's an advance. I don't think you could have said fifteen years ago that such a paradigm was really there. In the context of that paradigm you can now begin to rigorously test it against the observations elsewhere; that is, you can begin to make predictions about the process as a general phenomenon and see whether those predictions hold up."

The main controversy, though, is whether this is the correct model from which to work. The generalities of the theory fit nicely indeed, but many details still need to be explained. For example, three-quarters of all stars in the solar neighborhood are actually part of binary systems—that is, two stars that orbit each other. Why did *our* original cloud fragment form only one star—the sun? Why does a planet like Uranus spin on its side instead of the same direction as every other planet? And where did mysterious Pluto come from, and why doesn't it fit into any of the patterns? These are more than trivial questions.

If the idea that this planetary system formed as a natural consequence of one star's birth is correct, it would mean that the birth of other stars from cosmic clouds might also have spawned accompanying planets as well. If so, then the universe could literally be filled with similar systems just waiting to be discovered. In many ways, then, determining the likelihood of planetary systems in orbit around distant stars may depend on how typical a star the sun is.

OUR SUN, THE STAR

Anyone who has ever enjoyed a sun-drenched beach on a hot, summer day can sense the power of the sun. It generates a tremendous amount of energy—400 trillion trillion watts of power each second—enough to illuminate 2,600 Earths filled with 200-watt lightbulbs. Near its surface, where temperatures hover near 5,500 degrees Celsius, gigantic heat-carrying bubbles as large as Pennsylvania rise and sink in the solar atmosphere. Violent jets of superheated gas shoot upward for thousands of miles into space.

The sun's power has been known to every culture that ever lived on Earth. The ancients entrusted to the sun the personification of their most powerful gods. The source of this energy, however, is a question that has had to wait until modern times to be answered. One of the first to address this issue mathematically was the nineteenth-century German physicist Hermann Ludwig Ferdinand von Helmholtz.

Helmholtz wondered, since the most common energy source on Earth at the time was coal, whether the sun might be a gigantic furnace inside of which coal was being burned. He showed that, if the entire mass of the sun were made of coal and oxygen in the correct proportions, the resultant fire would keep the sun going at its present rate for only 1,500 years. Even with more efficient chemical reactions, Helmholtz could not figure how the sun could possibly have shone throughout the eons of historic and prehistoric times.

In 1853, he tried another approach. Suppose the sun were contracting slowly and releasing this change in potential energy as radiation. Helmholtz showed that, throughout the thousands of years of civilization, the sun would have contracted by only 0.06 percent—hardly a noticeable quantity even through the most powerful telescopes of the day. Since no better explanation had yet come along, the contracting sun of Helmholtz held sway for many years.

With the turn of the century came a young Austrian-born physicist named Albert Einstein, along with a complete change in perspectives. When Einstein calculated his now-famous equation $E = mc^2$ (where E represents energy, m represents mass, and c represents the velocity of light in a vacuum), he showed that matter and energy were merely manifestations of the same phenomenon—that matter was just a very concentrated form of energy and that they were, very simply put, interchangeable. Treat matter in the proper manner and you can convert it to pure energy.

In fact, a little can go a long, long way. For example, 1 gram of matter, if converted completely, would produce 21.5 trillion calories of energy—equivalent to that released by the chemical burning of 2.5 million liters of gasoline. If such a conversion were going on inside the sun and stars, scientists realized, they could easily explain its tremendous power over the many eons of time the sun has shone. However, this required not a chemical burning process but nuclear reactions within the sun to make it work. The reaction they proposed was called "fusion."

In the core of the sun, where temperatures soar to more than 10 million degrees, hydrogen atoms (which are about all that can exist under these intense conditions) race around at incredible speeds. When four hydrogen atoms slam into one another, they fuse to form two atoms of helium. But four helium atoms weigh *less* than the two of hydrogen that create them—about 4.8×10^{-29} kilograms less. This mass does not vanish but, instead, is transformed into energy by the fusion process and is described by Einstein's equation. The energy released does not seem terribly large—only about 4.3×10^{-12} joules—barely enough to raise a housefly less than 0.03 millimeter. But in the sun, where 10^{38} such reactions take place *each second,* the energy production is enormous. The sun has been burning at this rate for 5 billion years, and retains enough hydrogen fuel to continue for another 5 billion.

Other stars work the same way, but have differences that alter the rates at which they age. For example, massive bluish white supergiant stars contain fifteen to twenty times more material than the sun and, in order to hold up their heavy atmospheres, must convert their fuel to energy thousands of times faster. Even though they have a larger supply of hydrogen to consume, they do it in only millions of years. Much more common, however, are the stars known as red dwarfs, which contain only a fraction of a solar mass. With atmospheres this light, their internal engines burn at a much more leisurely pace and, as a result, these stars can last for hundreds of billions of years.

WHENCE CAME THE STARS?

If all stars function much like the sun, by the thermonuclear mechanism known as fusion, then perhaps all formed in similar ways as well, along with planetary families of their own. To find out, astronomers must explore the clouds of gas and dust that permeate interstellar space—regions similar to that where they believe the sun and its planetary system originated. The best place to look for newborn stars, it seems, is the Milky Way.

In trying to understand the nature of this mysterious glow that arches gracefully overhead on summer and autumn evenings, the ancients put forth a number of ideas. Some thought it was the scorched path of the sun on its daily jaunt across the sky. Others, particularly the Native Americans, imagined it as a roadway to heaven. The island dwellers of Polynesia saw it as a giant blue shark swimming overhead.

But aim a telescope or binoculars in its direction and its true nature becomes clear. It is composed of hundreds of millions of stars, punctuated occasionally by clumps of nebulosity. One of the first to make note of these nebulae was the eighteenth-century French comet hunter Charles Messier. In his relentless search for new comets, Messier continually stumbled across these hazy patches and mistook them for comets. To warn other comet hunters of these celestial "nuisances," Messier began listing them as objects to ignore if you were searching for comets. Ironically, Messier is known today not for his comet discoveries, but for his catalog of nebulous objects he deemed a waste of time.

Modern telescopes reveal the entries of Messier's catalog to be a variety of objects much more distant and exotic than any comet. Some turned out to be clusters of hundreds, thousands, or millions of stars within the Milky Way Galaxy; others were galaxies far beyond the Milky Way. Still others proved to be gargantuan clouds of gas and dust that appear quite intricately structured in long-exposure photographs. Some appear as thin as smoke twisted and stretched by a breeze while others are so thick that their great mass blocks from view all behind them, and they reveal themselves only in silhouette. Some scatter starlight through dust within and appear bluish in color. Others glow red—the telltale sign of hot hydrogen gas.

Yet, as different as each cloud appears, most share some common features. For example, when studied by radio and infrared telescopes, these hot clouds reveal chemical compositions of 75 percent hydrogen and nearly 25 percent helium, all intermingled with traces of carbon, nitrogen, oxygen, calcium, sodium, and heavier atoms. They appear to be composed of similar materials out of which the sun and its planetary system coalesced billions of years ago.

Within thicker, darker regions of these clouds, places through which even starlight cannot penetrate, the chemical composition is somewhat different. Here, more complex gases can exist as molecules. Many are simple compounds such as methane and ammonia, while others are much more elaborate: ethyl alcohol, formaldehyde, hydrogen cyanide, water, and carbon dioxide. To date, more than five dozen such compounds have been found within the dark clouds of interstellar nebulae—many of them organic in nature. Not only are gases present in these clouds; a tiny fraction of their mass is actually composed of dust grains about the size of particles in smoke, and made of carbon, iron, and silicates (rocklike minerals)—indeed, all the building blocks required to make stars, planets, even life itself.

Upon closer examination, astronomers have found that whenever they see a thick interstellar cloud, so, too, do they find in its vicinity bluish white supermassive stars, whose intense heat and high-energy radiation disrupt the gas and illuminate it from within. This phenomenon occurs far too frequently to be dismissed as mere coincidence.

One of the largest and nearest such nebula lies 1,500 light-years away in the direction of the constellation of Orion, and is known to every amateur astronomer as M42: the Great Nebula in Orion. Deep within its twisted mass of gas and dust lie the four bluish white stars of the Trapezium, the most massive of which weighs 40 times more than the sun and shines with 300,000 times its brilliance. These stars are known to be extremely young—perhaps only millions of years old—for if they were much older, their tremendous energy output would have long since exhausted their fuel supplies. Since the stars' motions have not carried them very far in this short time span, they must still lie near the places of their origin. Could it be that nebulae like Orion are indeed the sites of starbirth, just as current theories suggest? Is this the very material out of which stars and planets originate?

Even more evidence of starbirth comes from behind the clouds, out of view of traditional optical telescopes. Astronomers have used infrared and radio telescopes, combined with powerful computers, to peer through the nebulosity and construct a detailed map of the locations, velocities, and densities of more than twenty atomic hydrogen clouds and filaments in the Orion region. Here they found two great, dark clouds so cold and dense that molecules like carbon monoxide have formed in the shadows of dust particles. They dubbed them the Orion Molecular Clouds 1 and 2 (OMC-1 and OMC-2).

These molecular clouds contain at least a million atoms of hydrogen gas per cubic centimeter, along with tremendous amounts of dust. While this is far less than the 1×10^{19} atoms per cubic centimeter at sea level in the Earth's atmosphere, it is over 1,600 times more dense than the nebulosity in which the clouds are embedded. Deep within, warm compact centers seem to suggest that the clouds may now be collapsing. At the core of OMC-1 lie two intriguing objects. One, astronomers believe, is a young star still enshrouded by its dusty cocoon. The other, just to its south, is a cluster engulfed in an expanding shell of gas, and blasting in opposite directions two jets of hot gas at such a rate that it could only continue this process for a thousand years. This must, therefore, represent a group of even younger stars.

Another type of cloud that astronomers have found appears far less energetic and violent. Photographs of the nebulosity known as the Taurus-Auriga complex show tiny, dark, spherical "globules" embedded deep within the luminous cloud. These globules contain masses ranging anywhere from 10 to 10,000 times that of the sun within a volume of space barely 1 light-year across. While they appear dark to the eye, globules glow brilliantly to an infrared telescope, indicating that internal temperatures are quite high. Something is obviously happening on their insides, perhaps the rapid collapse of a protostar. In fact, studies of this complex suggest that, over the past 40 million years or so, stars like the sun have been constantly forming there.

Astronomers now believe that when a star finally ignites from within a globule and blows away its protective shroud, it shines with tremendous light. In recent years, many of these objects have been discovered emerging from such clouds. They are named T Tauri stars, after the first one ever found. As their newly found energy source tries to reach equilibrium with the weight of the star's atmosphere, T Tauri stars flicker wildly in brightness with periods of several days. In addition, they blast streams of hot luminous gas outward in two opposite directions—possibly the result of a spinning disk of material falling inward, dragging with it the magnetic field from the interstellar medium and forcing gases out the stars' poles of rotation.

Perhaps more common, however, are the so-called "naked" T Tauri stars, which outnumber their classical brethren by ten to one. These stars show no signs of being surrounded by dusty material, and they can be examined closely without interference from circumstellar "pollution." They raise a number of important questions. Have these stars moved so rapidly from their places of origin that they left behind their accompanying disks? Did a second star orbiting nearby disrupt their disks entirely? Were these stars spinning so rapidly that they ejected material completely, or so slowly that disks could never form in the first place? Whatever stripped this material from these stars must have done so remarkably quickly, for some naked T Tauri stars are believed to be younger than a million years old. Thus, unless planets can form extremely rapidly, it may be that only classical T Tauri stars could possibly develop such systems, and this would mean that only one-tenth of all low-mass and solar-type stars might produce planetary systems.

It appears that star formation from interstellar clouds is a common, natural phenomenon—at least in the solar neighborhood of the Milky Way galaxy. There seems to be enough visible matter in space to produce one new star for every ten existing ones. But if the universe is 20, or even 10, billion years old, this material should have long ago been exhausted. Why then do astronomers still see it? And why does star formation continue after all this time? The answers, its seems, come not from the process of stellar birth, but from the process of stellar death.

COSMIC RECYCLING

Stars spend about 90 percent of their lives converting hydrogen to helium—in other words, just being a star. Eventually, however, all stars run out of fuel and, when that day comes, their behavior must change. With no energy being produced at their cores to balance the inward pull of gravity, stars collapse under their own weight. What happens next depends entirely on the mass of the star, and how forcefully it collapses upon itself.

Most stars are tiny red dwarfs, with a luminosity barely one ten-thousandth that of the sun. For billions of years, a red dwarf star burns hydrogen and creates a reservoir of helium in its core. When the hydrogen is gone, the star collapses. Internal temperatures rise but not enough to begin the fusion of helium into carbon so instead, the star's gas pressure balances the weight of its atmosphere. This is where it ends. Slowly, the star radiates the last of its heat into space for billions—perhaps, trillions—of years, until one day it is gone from sight. Since these stars can live longer than the present age of the universe, none has ever been seen to die.

More massive stars meet a completely different fate. A star like the sun converts hydrogen to helium for 10 billion years. When it runs out of fuel, its core collapses and its atmosphere balloons to more than ten times its original size, turning the star into a red giant. As its core continues to collapse, it becomes hot enough—around 100 million degrees—that the helium "ash" itself fuses into carbon and oxygen. Eventually this, too, is gone, and the core collapses again. Now, however, the star puffs off its atmosphere, along with the vaporized materials of any planets nearby, in a series of explosions.

As cataclysmic as these events may seem, they are mild in comparison to the deaths of supermassive stars. Such "super-stars" exhaust their initial supply of hydrogen in 10 million years or so and they, too, become red giant stars. Unlike solar-type stars, the cores of supermassive stars collapse so violently that their internal temperatures rise to 600 million degrees—high enough for carbon fusion to occur in their cores. Some are blown apart by this process, while others continue to fuse oxygen, silicon, and even heavier elements in their cores. Each time a new element "ignites," it leaves behind a shell of lighter material surrounding it. But this cannot continue forever, and when the end comes, the star detonates in a colossal explosion: a supernova.

During the explosion, the star hurls its atmosphere into space, carrying with it hydrogen from the original star, along with heavy elements created during the star's death throes: helium, carbon, and oxygen. Along with these "normal" elements are even heavier ones that were created during the explosion itself: gold, uranium, and other rare elements. As these shells expand outward, they intermingle with interstellar clouds, seeding them with heavy elements and triggering the collapse of globules into new stars, dusty disks, and, possibly, planetary systems.

* * *

HOW COMMON ARE PLANETS?

Everywhere telescopes are aimed, astronomers detect evidence that stars and planetary systems originate in purely natural and nonextraordinary ways. Solar-type stars are plentiful, and many appear to be surrounded by dusty disks from which planets may form. In addition, the chemical elements and molecules of worlds and of life seem plentiful throughout interstellar space. Everything seems to suggest that planets and planetary systems should be common. Before the birth of extrasolar planets can be proved, though, astronomers must consider that most stars form not as single units, but as binary or multiple star systems.

Computer modeling suggests that binary and multiple star systems may not be a very likely home for planets, since the star formation process can produce either a binary system or a disk out of which planets might coalesce, but not both. The reason is that if a second or third star is formed, any protoplanetary disks that happen to exist are entirely disrupted by the erratic gravitational forces caused by the moving stars. From this it seems that if binaries or multiple stars are the rule, then planetary systems must be the exception.

But suppose a star happened to wander by an existing planetary system at just the right distance; it might be captured and trapped into a very large elliptical orbit, one in which all bodies might remain stable. In fact, some astronomers have speculated that the sun has such a stellar companion. Named Nemesis, this so-far-invisible body is postulated to swing inward toward the sun periodically and disrupt the clouds of comets near the edge of the solar system, sending them careening inward to collide with the inner planets. It was just such a collision that some suggest might have caused the demise of the dinosaurs 65 million years ago, as well as a number of other mass extinctions that have occurred at regular intervals. Yet, judging from the distances between the stars in the sun's galactic neighborhood, such a stellar capture seems unlikely at best.

WHERE DO WE SEARCH?

From evidence gathered over the past few decades, most astronomers now believe that planets and planetary systems are common throughout the galaxy, and they have begun to contemplate ways to find them. But where does the search begin?

At first, one might think that old stars would be the best candidates, since planetary systems would have had more time to evolve and, therefore, more might exist. It must be remembered, however, that the earliest generations of stars were formed long before the interstellar medium had become enriched with heavy elements by exploding stars. Perhaps planets cannot even form without these materials forming their cores. The youngest stars are also a possibility, since these have the most abundant heavy elements of all. However, the hottest of stars have such short life spans that planetary systems may never have time to form before the star tears itself, and its protoplanetary system, apart. The coolest, low-mass stars may never have had enough mass to form a protoplanetary disk in the first place. The most promising candidate stars, it seems, are those most like the sun in age and mass since such a system is, at least, possible.

If astronomers should ever find bodies in orbit around another star, how can they determine whether they are planets, super-low-mass stars, or even brown dwarfs? One way is to look for patterns similar to those found in *this* solar system. For example, if the objects orbit the star in roughly circular, coplanar orbits, they are most likely planets. Astronomers could look for a distribution of masses similar to those here, with the most massive planets lying near the middle of the system. They could examine the chemical composition of the bodies to see whether or not they differ from that of their parent star. They might even try to detect the dusty disk surrounding a star out of which planets might one day form.

Discovering just one such system would immediately demonstrate that ours is but one example of a general class of systems that must exist everywhere, and would give impetus to an ambitious search program. Finding nothing would cast doubt on the prevalence of such structures, and it would call into question the most fundamental theories of star and planet formation.

Either way, the search would be exciting.

5

It rose atop a roaring fountain of fire into the black California sky. Below, hundreds of people at the Vandenberg Air Force Base gazed upward to watch the spectacle, and countless others from around the southwestern United States watched as the last remaining glimmers of twilight illuminated the rocket's smoky trail. Within minutes, the fiery sight vanished among the stars— its smoke dispersed by the winds—and the curious who watched on that night of January 25, 1983, headed home with thrilling memories of a once-in-a-lifetime experience.

For scientists, however, the excitement had only begun, for atop the McDonnell Douglas Delta 3910 rocket rode a sophisticated new telescope that was designed to view the universe like never before. Its name was the Infrared Astronomy Satellite— IRAS for short.

IRAS was a telescope like none other. A joint project of the United States, the United Kingdom, and the Netherlands, this $200 million satellite was designed to map the heavens by using the radiation from a region of the electromagnetic spectrum never before seen in detail—the faint and ghostly glow of the infrared.

Infrared is a low-energy radiation—more commonly known as heat—which lies just beyond the red portion of the visible spectrum and possesses wavelengths ranging from a thousandth of a millimeter in the "near"-infrared to nearly a full millimeter long in the "far"-infrared. Everything on Earth and in space emits in the infrared, no matter how hot or cold it seems. Hot objects like stars emit not only light, but infrared radiation as well. Cooler material, like the thick clouds of interstellar dust that permeate the space between the stars, are not hot enough to emit visible radiation, and appear to optical telescopes as forever-dark material in silhouette against brighter distant clouds. But to an infrared telescope, these interstellar dust clouds glow brilliantly, and by studying their infrared images and spectra, astronomers can glean clues about the clouds' sizes, temperatures, and physical and chemical makeup.

Scientists have long used ground-based telescopes to search for infrared radiation coming from deep within thick, dusty regions of space where stars' nuclear fires have not yet ignited, and from the turbulent activity inside distant galactic nuclei. They even have used it to search for unseen companions around nearby stars such as VB8. Still, success has never come easily for infrared astronomers. Water vapor and other gases in the Earth's atmosphere block much of this radiation from view, so the vision of ground-based telescopes is restricted to certain wavelengths of IR radiation that can survive their trip to the ground. The only good views of the infrared universe have come from telescopes carried high above the obscuring atmosphere on short rocket flights, in specially modified jet aircraft, or in high-altitude balloons. None of these has ever provided more than a fleeting glimpse of the mysterious infrared sky.

With the launching of IRAS, however, astronomers had the telescope of their dreams. Its sophisticated array of electronic detectors and instruments was to orbit the Earth at an altitude of 900 kilometers for as long as a year and survey the entire sky in four distinct infrared wavelength bands. It would make the first far-infrared "road map" of the heavens, on which all future studies could be based.

By terrestrial standards, IRAS was small—its radiation-gathering mirror measuring little more than half a meter across—but from its perch high above the obscuring atmosphere, the telescope would be able to see infrared sources a thousand times fainter than had ever been seen before. In fact, its detectors were so sensitive that they could discern the heat of a single flashlight bulb more than 3,000 kilometers away.

Not only was this unprecedented sensitivity a remarkable feature of this instrument, it was also a severe disadvantage, for the faint radiations the telescope would be seeking could easily be overwhelmed by its own heat loss. To prevent the telescope and scientific instruments from appearing "red-hot" to their own eyes, engineers surrounded the spacecraft telescopes with a vessel filled with superfluid helium, one of the best heat conductors known. The idea was that, as the surrounding helium absorbed heat from the telescope, it would boil off into space, carrying with it unwanted heat and maintaining the telescope's temperature at a mere 2 degrees above absolute zero (-271 degrees Celsius).

OPENING ITS EYE

When IRAS reached its final altitude, ground controllers carefully maneuvered the 1,043-kilogram instrument into a permanent circular orbit directly over the Earth's day-night dividing line. From this vantage point, the telescope was always aimed at right angles to the dangerous rays of the sun, while its solar panels could face sunward and collect energy to power the scientific and communications instruments. After settling the telescope into its ninety-minute orbit, scientists began an exhaustive check of all the systems aboard. Finally, on February 1, 1983, with all telescope systems operating as planned, scientists on the ground commanded IRAS to remove its protective aperture cover and open its eye to the universe. Within only minutes, IRAS began to gather infrared radiation from the universe at an unbelievable rate. By the end of its first day of operation, IRAS had logged some four thousand infrared sources—twice the number that had been previously cataloged.

Astronomers continued their work with IRAS, scanning the skies in search of infrared secrets and gathering 2 million bits of data every hour. The flood of incoming data was stored on an onboard computer tape and "dumped" twice each day as the spacecraft passed over the tracking station at Chilton, England, then relayed electronically to NASA's Jet Propulsion Laboratory in Pasadena, California, for processing.

During its eleven-month scrutiny of the heavens, IRAS radioed to Earth more than 200 billion bits of data and mapped nearly 95 percent of the sky. Among the 200,000 never-before-detected infrared sources it discovered around the sky, IRAS found five new comets, three giant rings of dust in the solar system, huge dust shells around the bright star Betelgeuse in the shoulder of Orion, and a mysterious asteroid or dead comet little more than 1 kilometer across that sweeps nearer the sun than any other known object. This was only the beginning, for buried within the mass of IRAS data stored in earthbound computers, one more discovery lay in wait—the discovery that this family of planets may not be unique.

WHAT'S THAT WE SEE?

In August of 1983, eight months after the telescope's launch, at the IRAS tracking and data acquisition center at the Rutherford Appleton Laboratory in England, astronomers H. H. Aumann of NASA's Jet Propulsion Laboratory and Fred Gillett of the Kitt Peak National Observatory began their observations with calibrations of the telescope by aiming it in the direction of the bright summertime star Vega. Only 26 light-years distant, Vega is one of the brightest and most studied stars in the heavens and has become a standard against which other stars' properties are measured.

As the data from IRAS came in, Gillett and Aumann noticed something peculiar. The amount of visible light radiated by Vega was perfectly normal, but the telescope was sensing about sixteen times more infrared radiation coming from the direction of Vega than the astronomers had expected to find. Until now, Vega was considered to be among the most ordinary of stars. Less than a billion years old, its only peculiarity, it seemed, was that it rotated more slowly than other stars of its type. Its display of such an "infrared excess" was a mystery.

In trying to understand the data, the astronomers began asking themselves some questions. Did a distant, faint star, interstellar cloud, or galaxy somehow park itself along the same line of sight as Vega, either in front of or behind the star, spilling its own infrared energy onto the detector? Was the star's atmosphere so active that it produces radio waves and infrared by nonthermal radiation processes? Was there an unseen source of the radiation in orbit about the star itself? To find out, Aumann and Gillett carefully observed the area around Vega and measured the size of the emitting region. They found that the source appeared spread out over some 20 arc seconds of the sky, which, at the distance of Vega, represents a span of nearly 13 billion kilometers on either side of the star. The heat it produced suggested that its source had a temperature of only -185 degrees Celsius, much like that of the icy particles within the innermost rings of Saturn.

Whatever the source of this "extra" radiation, it was most certainly not a typical star, but most likely a mass of solid material in the vicinity of Vega itself. As sensitive as IRAS was, however, its infrared eye could not discern any fine details within. For that, scientists were forced to make educated guesses based on what they *could* detect. They soon came up with several possibilities.

Some suggested that a single large body might be orbiting the star and emitting the excess infrared detected by IRAS. But the word "large" was a fantastic understatement. To account for the observed heat, astronomers calculated that such a body must be sixty-two times larger than the star itself; yet, even with that immense size, it would represent only 1 percent of the area from which they detected radiation. The only way researchers could make theory square with their observations was if Vega were accompanied not by a single solid body, but rather by a swarm of smaller particles that absorbed light from the star and reradiated it away as heat.

The radiation emitted by a mass depends strongly upon its surface area; a single, large body has a finite surface area that emits a finite amount of infrared radiation. Grind that body into dust, however, and the surface area capable of emitting radiation into space increases tremendously. This means that a cloud of small particles can emit much more infrared radiation than a solid body of equal mass. The issue, then, becomes how small the particles needed to be. Calculations showed that the disk could not be composed of typical interstellar grains, for the number of dirty silicate grains only 0.04 millimeter across required to emit the radiation observed at Vega would produce a disk 200 arc seconds, or 130 billion kilometers, across—ten times larger than the measured size of the emitting region. In addition, such tiny particles would have long ago been either blasted away by the star's intense radiation or sucked inward by its powerful gravity. To account for their observations, astronomers figured that the star must be encircled by a 24-billion-kilometer-wide disk of particles ranging from the size of buckshot to asteroids, moons, and, possibly, planets.

Finally, astronomers had a straightforward and simple explanation—a theory that supported the notion that the sun might not be the only star surrounded by solid bodies at least a millimeter across. The one thing the theory didn't explain was, why? Why did this disk exist in the first place? The material could not have been blasted directly from the star itself, and its large particle size ruled out interstellar space as its origin. Where, then, did it originate? The answer, it seemed, might be found in the birth of Vega itself.

A NEWBORN SOLAR SYSTEM?

Because Vega is such a hot star, with a surface temperature of nearly 10,000 degrees Celsius, it is a relative newcomer on the cosmic scene. Born only about 300 million years ago, its embryonic cloud of gas and dust whirled itself into the infrared-radiating disk visible today. With a mass of anywhere from 300 solar masses down to that of the solar system, the cloud's particles eventually began to collide, stick together, and grow into larger and larger bodies—much like our own planetary system evolved from its birth 5 billion years ago. Unlike the sun, however, Vega is a relative youngster and, since full-fledged planets may require from 10 million to a billion years to form completely, Vega may not yet have had sufficient time for its disk material to coalesce into large planetary bodies. So, if astronomers' explanation of Vega's infrared excess was correct, the disk they found around the star could represent a planetary system in the process of forming—a momentous discovery at least.

Finding such a primordial solar system around an otherwise unremarkable star only 26 light-years distant was, indeed, a surprise. It provided astronomers a unique laboratory in which to test their theories about the origin and evolution of a solar system and how common the process might be. It suggested that many other stars might also be accompanied by planetary disks that have long remained hidden from view, and that the Milky Way might contain millions in various stages of evolution just waiting to be discovered.

This exciting prospect prompted astronomers to study the IRAS data more closely, and it wasn't long before they found more than fifty similar infrared-excess stars scattered about the heavens. Some turned out to be well-known astrometric binaries, with the infrared excess coming from the unseen companion stars. Others, like Fomalhaut, the brightest star in the autumn constellation of Piscis Austrinus, were somewhat older and cooler than Vega. These were more likely to be disks that have experienced ongoing planet-building for eons, perhaps even containing worlds on which life may have already emerged.

SEEING THESE DISKS

As remarkable as these discoveries proved to be, they only marked the beginning. Astronomers realized that while infrared instruments could sense the heat emanating from the dusty material near a star, optical telescopes might actually be able to *see* the star's light being scattered from a disk's colder, outlying regions. It was not long before they put powerful ground-based instruments to work on the problem.

In mid-April of 1984, astronomers Bradford Smith, then of the University of Arizona, and Richard Terrile, of NASA's Jet Propulsion Laboratory, (JPL) armed themselves with a list of four infrared-excess stars that had been found by IRAS and set out to *see* the disks in visible light. Their plan was simple: they would block the light of each star's image with a tiny circular mask and use sensitive electronic detectors to photograph any surrounding disks that shone through.

The instrument they were using was called a coronagraph, a modification of the basic instrument designed by the French astrophysicist Bernard Lyot in 1930 for photographing the solar corona, the normally invisible outer atmosphere of the sun. In a classical coronagraph, a miniature eclipse is produced in the telescope, enabling astronomers to study the corona—without having to wait for a rare total solar eclipse to pass over their observatories. But even the best coronagraph does not produce a perfect image. "You still can't get rid of the scattered light around the star itself," explains Smith. "That's caused in the Earth's atmosphere and you're stuck with it. About the best you can do is try to get to a good site where the air is relatively clean."

So that's just what Smith and Terrile did. They attached their equipment to the 2.5-meter du Pont telescope at Las Campanas Observatory near La Serena, Chile. Las Campanas is located at an altitude of 2,300 meters in the Andes of Chile, one of the darkest, steadiest, and most spectacular sites on Earth for the use of precision data-gathering techniques.

Their primary objective while in Chile was to search for moons and rings of the planets Uranus and Neptune, but just in case the opportunity arose, they took with them their list of four infrared-excess stars. As it turned out, this was a good idea. "Right at the beginning of the evening, we had a small sliver of dark time before the moon came up," recalls Smith. "Since one of these stars was observable, we used the equipment to look at it." The star they chose was Beta Pictoris, a rather unremarkable star 53 light-years from Earth. To those living throughout much of the Earth's Northern Hemisphere, "Beta Pic," as astronomers affectionately call it, remains permanently below the southern horizon. But from the observatory in Chile, Beta Pic shone faintly overhead in the constellation of Pictor, the artist's easel.

During their observations, the astronomers continually compared the light of Beta Pic with that of an adjacent star—one, presumably, with no disk around it. Later, the digitized images would be divided one into the other with the hope that any extra light near Beta Pictoris would stand out noticeably in the photos. At the time, however, the image of Beta Pic looked perfectly normal. "When we first saw [it] through the telescope, we didn't know what we had," recalls Terrile. That was about to change.

After their observing run, the astronomers returned to their respective institutions to reduce their data. At JPL, Terrile began to apply special computer enhancement techniques to the five-minute exposures to remove the effects of starlight scattered by the Earth's atmosphere. "After I did the ratios, I got very excited when I saw these two little appendages sticking out from behind the mask," he recalls.

The "appendages" were, indeed, stunning. Extending outward from both sides of the mask were streaks of light nearly a minute of arc from end to end. A quick calculation showed that, at the distance of Beta Pictoris, this corresponded to a disk 60 billion kilometers across—ten times larger than our own solar system—and nearly three times larger than the disk around Vega that IRAS had measured a year earlier. This was not surprising, however, since IRAS detected only the heat reradiated from the inner part of a disk, while the optical photo had captured visible starlight being scattered far from the glare of a star.

Terrile's excitement was perhaps magnified by the fact that the astronomers never really expected to see anything. "It was totally exploratory," recalls Terrile, "but you [never] know until you look. Here was a star with an infrared excess. [Was] there a visible component to it, [and was it] organized in any geometric way that [would] tell us something about the star? The answer to these questions [turned out to be] yes. It was a flattened disk of material! The adrenaline really pumped when I first saw it," he recalled, "but it was a little scary in the sense that it had the potential of being something very exciting, but also some kind of erroneous [artifact]. We didn't want to report it until we knew."

Fortunately, all checked out, and the result remained. "In fact," says Terrile, "when we looked at it again with other telescopes, it [was] always there. It's a very believable phenomenon now."

NOW, AN EXPLANATION

Astronomers now believe that the photo shows a disk of dust and ice particles, the bulk of which are much too cold for even IRAS to have detected, ranging in size from microscopic grains of less than 0.03 millimeter to chunks perhaps a few kilometers across. Their composition probably includes water ices, silicates, and carbonaceous organic compounds, and possibly molecular hydrogen, the same materials from which *our* planetary system formed 4.5 billion years ago. Of course this, in itself, does not firmly prove that the disk is a primordial planetary system in orbit around Beta Pictoris but, based on the accepted model of our own solar system's birth, astronomers believe that the particles there should collide, stick together, and begin building planets in less than 100 million years.

There is yet another property of the disk that leads astronomers to believe that it must be very young: the fact that it appears so flat. An older disk that has been gravitationally disturbed by mature planets would not appear nearly as flat, and much of the remaining particulate debris would long ago have been ejected into interplanetary space. Nevertheless, some researchers suspect that the disk, while very young, may be old enough that planet-building could already have begun inside.

Evidence comes from the fortunate coincidence that allows earthbound observers to view this disk nearly edge on. By measuring the density of the particles from the edges of the disk inward, astronomers have found that it increases steadily toward the center. The unusually thick material through which the star's light must pass on its way toward Earth should change significantly the characteristics of that light. The larger dust particles would scatter its blue light, and produce a redder star than would be expected for its type, a phenomenon seen frequently as the sun sets every evening. "But Beta Pic appears very much like a normal star of its type," explains Brad Smith. "This suggests that the area within some [4.5 billion kilometers] of the star—the very region where planets have formed in *our* solar system—must be relatively clear of dust. And this could have profound implications for planetary theorists."

Why such a "hole" should exist in this disk, or in those found around the stars Vega and Fomalhaut, had astronomers considering all sorts of phenomena. One seemed most intriguing to astronomers. "One of the ways these holes could be formed and maintained," explains Dana Backman of the Kitt Peak National Observatory, "is if planets have already formed within. [They] would have swept up dusty material and cleared out the inner regions of the disk. This type of particle cloud, which used to be considered a sign of ongoing planet formation, may instead be the *aftermath* of planet formation."

In fact, recent observations of the Beta Pictoris disk show that it is both larger and less symmetrical than previously believed, spanning 135 billion kilometers in one direction and 165 billion in the other. This, astronomers postulate, may be caused by a large body orbiting in a noncircular path and pulling material to one side of the disk. Calculations suggest that to create this observed asymmetry a body at least the size of Earth is required.

Of course, no one has ever seen any such bodies in orbit around Beta Pictoris, but some find it difficult to ignore the circumstantial evidence. "It's my intuitive feeling that this is, indeed, another solar system," says Brad Smith. "Up until now this has never been demonstrated. There's been no hard evidence that we in our own solar system are not unique, [that ours is not] some one-time-only happening. But here's evidence that we're not at all alone. Older stars like the [sun] may have already formed planets and swept up or blown away the [dusty] material, whereas the younger ones [seem] caught in that stage of their life where it's still visible. I think we're going to find that the formation of planets—of solar systems—is a natural phase of the formation of a star."

ARE THERE MORE OUT THERE?

After scouring the IRAS data in search of infrared-excess stars, researchers discovered that the phenomenon is quite common, and naturally became curious about the frequency of circumstellar disks among the stars of the solar neighborhood. So in 1986, Kitt Peak astronomers Dana Backman and Frederick Gillett, along with Frank Low of the University of Arizona, began a systematic search to find out.

They used IRAS data coupled with ground-based infrared observations made at Kitt Peak to search 134 stars within 17 light-years of Earth for infrared excesses that might be caused by dust clouds or other heat-radiating material. They found that as many as one or two out of every ten young stars in our neck of the galactic woods may be encircled by such a disk—just what one would expect if disks survive half a billion years before planets form. And not only young stars, either. Several appeared to be older than 2 billion years—some even as old as the sun—indicating that the particle cloud phenomenon is not unique to young stars, and is not necessarily evidence of ongoing planetary accretion. In fact, the sun itself may be surrounded by such a cloud, but it would be extremely difficult to detect from within unless it were as dense and bright as that around Beta Pictoris.

For those who had hoped for and expected to find a planetary system around every star, 20 percent may seem slim pickings indeed. On the other hand, those who feared that conditions favoring planet formation occurred around only one star in a million should be quite pleased. The numbers speak even louder against those who believe catastrophic theories. "The real significance of this," explains Smith, "is that a large segment of the population, including many scientists, believe that our solar system is unique—that something funny happened in the solar cloud to form planets. This shows that if there's one more solar system out there, then there surely must be others. We hope to find more of these and study them. Eventually, if we have enough, we might be able to see a whole spectrum of objects."

By now, astronomers everywhere had caught the "planetary fever." Papers, research proposals, and entire conferences were dedicated to the existence of brown dwarfs, circumstellar disks, and extrasolar planets. More and more astronomers were turning their eyes skyward to try to be the first to find one. The race had begun.

6

EVERYBODY'S SEARCHING

With the IRAS discovery of dusty disks in orbit around a number of nearby stars now dramatically confirmed by visual images of Beta Pictoris, a coherent picture was emerging of planetary systems as a natural result of the star formation process. After all, such material was regarded as a likely precursor to the formation of actual planets and, since stars abound in the Milky Way galaxy, planetary systems like our own might also be common. When the Beta Pic findings were coupled with the earlier astrometric evidence that brown dwarfs, and possibly even large planets, also orbit other stars, the search for extrasolar planetary systems suddenly blossomed.

Armed with ever more powerful telescopic instrumentation and observational strategies, astronomers began an all-out race to be the first to discover planets in orbit around other stars. They employed many creative techniques with the hopes of detecting planets either directly by their own light emission or indirectly through their gravitational influence on their parent star. As new discoveries poured in from a variety of fronts and coverage in the popular press grew rapidly, so did controversy among scientists over the validity of tantalizing new results.

CIRCUMSTELLAR DISKS

As discussed earlier, T Tauri stars are thought to represent the earliest stages of stellar life. In some cases, they appear to be surrounded by debris left over from the process of star formation, debris that could eventually lead to the formation of planets.

A case in point is the star named HL Tauri. Located some 500 light-years from Earth, this star may be only between 100,000 and 1 million years old. Compared with the age of the sun, 5 billion years, this star must have only recently emerged from its nebulous womb. Astronomers' first inkling that the star was unusual came decades ago. While studying its infrared spectrum, they found the presence of ice particles at the star. Since ice could not possibly exist within the star's hot atmosphere, the discoverers reasoned that the newly found ice must be part of a colder disk of material remaining from the collapse of the star out of the interstellar medium.

It wasn't until the 1960s, however, that photos of this star showed gaseous material in the area; unfortunately, nothing resembling a disk could be found. This is not surprising since, at the distance of this star, a disk the size of the solar system would appear—even through the largest ground-based telescopes—smaller than the overexposed image of the star itself.

Then, in 1984, the technology to see such disks was turned on this star. Using speckle interferometry to remove the blurring caused by the Earth's turbulent atmosphere, astronomers took the first image of this star and its disk. From the amount and color of the disk's light, they learned that the disk contained sufficient matter to form a planetary system similar to our own.

As often occurs in science, this discovery raised more questions than it answered. Is this material bound by the star's gravity and confined in orbit around the star? Could it possibly be a preplanetary disk? Or is the material just coincidentally aligned along the same line of sight as the star but at a totally different distance with no physical connection at all?

To find out, astronomers decided to search the star's radio spectrum for lines of carbon monoxide, a molecule known to be plentiful in the vicinity of young stars. Unfortunately, one radio telescope aimed in the direction of this star would not produce a resolution great enough to see detail and motions within the disk. Instead, astronomers needed several radio telescopes linked together electronically to produce the imaging power of a single dish as wide as the array itself. They chose three radio telescopes at the Owens Valley Radio Observatory in central California.

Images created from this array showed an elongated disk around the star eighty times larger than the known size of our solar system. By studying the Doppler shifts of the spectral lines (see page 34), astronomers not only were able to measure the overall velocity of the star and disk together as they moved through space, they also found that the material at various points within the disk was moving at different speeds. The disk material appeared to be gravitationally bound to the star itself and also to be orbiting the star in a fashion similar to that of the matter within our own solar system.

The details of this motion were first predicted by the German mathematician Johannes Kepler, who, in the seventeenth century, calculated the motions of the planets. In his three laws of motion, Kepler showed that bodies in orbit around the sun move at different speeds, depending on their distances from the sun. Mercury, the closest planet to the sun, moves fastest, while distant Pluto moves the slowest. Indeed, the spectral observations of HL Tauri showed that the disk orbits its star with Keplerian motion—with the inner material orbiting fastest, and the farthest material orbiting the slowest—and demonstrated without a doubt that the disk is bound by gravity to the star and is revolving around it, just as one would expect for orbiting material about to begin planet formation.

Still another scheme for deducing the presence of circumstellar disks was devised by Professor Stephen Strom and his colleagues at the University of Massachusetts at Amherst. Their plan was to search for possible disklike planetary environments by using spectroscopy to study the stars' "stellar wind."

All stars, including the sun, blast copious amounts of material into space in the form of a steady stellar wind. Since this material flows outward from a star in all directions, equal amounts of this material should appear to be both approaching and receding from an observer. However, if the view of the star's environment is partially blocked, say by an otherwise invisible, but tilted, circumstellar disk, the view of its wind would also be partially blocked. It was this very effect that Strom hoped to find. He describes it as if the star-disk system were an LP record with an orange at the center. "If this 'record' is tilted toward the Earth," he explains, "a high-velocity stream of particles would be seen squirting from only the top of the 'orange.' The opaque, extended disk of gas and dust, or 'record,' would mask any wind emerging from the other side of the star."

Of the twenty young stars examined by Strom, sixteen followed this pattern, indicating that protoplanetary disks may be fairly common companions of young stars. All is not so clearly understood about this phenomenon, though, for some of these stars seem to be as old as 3 million years. Why haven't their circumstellar disks yet dissipated in planetary formation? Current models of this process predict that planets should have begun forming, and the disk should have begun to disappear, in only one-tenth of that time.

STAR CLUSTERS YOUNG AND OLD

Of all the disks that have thus far been found around the sky, how many have or will spawn planetary systems? The answer remains unknown, since the amount of material in these circumstellar disks, as well as their efficiency in accreting this material into planets, is difficult to measure. To understand better the evolution of circumstellar disks, Strom and his colleagues studied eighty-three solar-type stars embedded within the dark interstellar clouds near the border between the constellations Taurus and Auriga. Their idea was simple: if circumstellar disks do eventually become planetary systems, then disks should be most common around the youngest of stars. The older the stars they observe, the fewer disks they should see.

What they found was most significant. Half of those stars younger than 3 million years emitted far more infrared radiation than astronomers would have expected from the stars alone, suggesting the presence of dusty circumstellar material in their vicinity. Of those stars believed to be about 10 million years old, only 10 percent showed an infrared excess. The results suggest that if all these stars had begun their lives surrounded by circumstellar disks, the disks have somehow been destroyed over time—perhaps by the formation of planets.

Adding even more corroboration to the evidence, Strom's study found three disks whose infrared emissions indicate the presence of holes or gaps in their interiors, nearest to their stars. This behavior, similar to that seen earlier in the material around Beta Pictoris, could be explained if planets have already begun to sweep up material there.

TAKING ANOTHER TACK

The observations of circumstellar disks provided indirect evidence that planets may well be forming around other stars, and that older stars may now have mature planetary systems similar to that around the sun. If astronomers could detect actual planetary bodies orbiting such stars, this theory would be strengthened considerably.

It was just such a detection that William Forrest of the University of Rochester was hoping for when his team of astronomers began an infrared survey of sixty nearby faint stars in search of cool, dim companions. On the evening of July 28, 1985, Forrest aimed the 3-meter telescope of the Infrared Telescope Facility (IRTF) on Mauna Kea at a faint red star known as Gliese 569. An extremely tiny, red point of light that looked for all the world like a companion body appeared only 5 arc seconds north of the star. If this new object were at the same distance as Gliese 569 (34 light-years), then it was intrinsically much brighter than other low-mass stars known around the sky. If this were true, the team believed, then they had found either an extremely low-mass star just beginning to come to grips with its newly found internal energy source or a young brown dwarf. Before they could determine that, however, an even more important question required an answer. Was this companion actually bound by gravity to the star Gliese 569, or was it a more distant star that, coincidentally, appeared along the same line of sight?

Gliese 569 had been observed for many years and had never shown any wobbling motion that would have suggested the possibility of a companion object orbiting nearby. This was not surprising, however, because at its apparent distance from Gliese 569, one orbit (and therefore, one "wiggle" of the primary star) would require some 500 years. So, to learn if the object was in fact a companion body, the astronomers watched the star's motion carefully for more than two years. During that time Gliese 569 drifted in proper motion about 0.71 arc seconds across the sky and, even though there was no wobbling, the mystery object followed right along. Thus, the researchers determined, these two bodies (Gliese 569-A and B) seemed to be a single system bound together by mutual gravity.

Of course, one final question remained. What kind of object is the companion? Is it a tiny red dwarf star or a substellar brown dwarf—the first ever found? The only way to know for sure is to measure its mass by watching both bodies' motions around their common center of gravity. With an apparent speed of only 0.06 arc seconds per year, the companion requires only a few years for its motion to become noticeable. But the primary star, being much more massive, moves five to ten times more slowly and requires decades to spot. The pair must be watched carefully through a significant portion of its orbit before the masses, and therefore the true nature of Gliese 569-B, can be determined.

Another approach to estimating the mass of Gliese 569-B is much more indirect. Through calculations of the physics at work inside brown dwarfs, astronomers can predict how the object's brightness changes with mass and age. The calculations show that these bodies begin their lives very warm, possibly even warm enough to glow in visible light. Since thermonuclear reactions never begin in their cores, however, their apparent brightness decreases steadily with age. A red dwarf star, on the other hand, eventually stabilizes and shines constantly for the rest of its life. Depending on the age of Gliese 569-B, it could be either a young brown dwarf (if it were 200 to 300 million years old) or an old red dwarf (more than a billion years old). In between these ages, the object could be either type.

Determining the age of an individual star is difficult but, because the bodies in a binary system are thought to form together from the same interstellar cloud, the age of Gliese 569-B can be estimated, in principle, from observed properties of its primary red dwarf star Gliese 569-A. For example, a rapid rotation rate, high amounts of lithium in its atmosphere, and active flaring usually indicate a young object, while a rapid velocity through the galaxy and a low abundance of elements heavier than helium are indications of greater age (several billion years). These age indicators all suggest that Gliese 569-A is relatively young, perhaps somewhere between 70 million and 600 million years old.

Although the numbers remained uncertain, it seemed possible that the companion represented the first brown dwarf ever found. The news media, unwilling to wait the years necessary for direct verification, descended on the team and began to publish stories about their discovery of the first brown dwarf—possibly even the first extrasolar planet—just as they did with McCarthy and VB8-B little more than a year earlier. Only time will tell if they were correct.

COMPANIONS TO WHITE DWARFS

Ironically, as Forrest pursued his work on Gliese 569-B, Professor Ben Zuckerman of UCLA was conducting a different search, also using the IRTF telescope. Unlike Forrest, who imaged the regions around faint red dwarf stars in the solar neighborhood of the Milky Way, Zuckerman and his colleague Dr. Eric E. Becklin of the University of Hawaii used a technique called infrared photometry to search the environments of *white* dwarf stars for signs of excess infrared emission.

White dwarfs represent the final stage of life for stars like the sun. Upon exhausting their central fuel, these stars swell into red giants hundreds of millions of miles across, then blow their atmospheres into space and collapse to become hot, white stars the size of Earth: white dwarfs. Because surface temperatures of white dwarf stars are much hotter than that of the sun, their infrared emissions are relatively weak. In contrast, a cooler brown dwarf emits most of its energy in the infrared portion of the spectrum and, therefore, should be easy to detect near a white dwarf star.

After searching the vicinities of several hundred white dwarfs in the young, nearby clusters known as the Hyades and the Pleiades, both of which showed few promising results, Zuckerman and his team decided to turn their gaze toward isolated white dwarfs. In the early morning hours of August 24, 1987, they found something intriguing.

The star they were observing was known as Giclas 29-38, a white dwarf located just 46 light-years away in the direction of the constellation Pisces. The infrared radiation they received was similar to what one might expect for a star with a temperature of 11,500 degrees Kelvin, but there was a little left over—an amount that the emissions from the star alone couldn't explain. They reasoned that something near the star must be contributing to the excess.

Unfortunately, the morning sky was draped with thin patchy clouds, and the astronomers couldn't trust their observations. By the following morning the sky had cleared, and the astronomers anxiously aimed their telescope toward the star again. Sure enough, the results were the same. Something in the direction of the white dwarf was contributing to the infrared excess and was radiating at a temperature of only 1,200 degrees Kelvin.

To determine the radiation's exact point of origin, the astronomers scanned the area around the star. They soon found that the vast majority of radiation emanated from within only 1 arc second of the white dwarf itself. While the probability that some distant star or galaxy was shining along nearly the same line of sight and influencing their observations was small, it was not zero. So, to check this possibility, the researchers examined old photographs of the region obtained during an all-sky photographic survey performed at the Palomar Observatory in the 1940s and 1950s. Of course, in the intervening decades, the relatively nearby white dwarf had moved slightly among the more distant stars and galaxies and, so, on the photos, the object appeared in a different place than it did at the time of the research. But when the astronomers checked the plates for the then-current location of the white dwarf, they found absolutely no other star or galaxy in the area. Whatever was producing the infrared emissions they found must be traveling with the white dwarf itself.

A fundamental problem remained. Did the excess infrared energy originate from a single companion object or, perhaps, from a dusty disk warmed by light from the central star? To many astronomers a brown dwarf companion seemed an unlikely prospect because any material originally orbiting the primary star would have been incinerated while the primary star was a red giant some 600 million years ago. At the very least, they felt, the red giant's atmosphere would have slowed the body's orbital motion and caused it to spiral inward toward the stellar core.

Also unlikely was a "black dwarf" companion, an old white dwarf that had cooled and faded from view. The cooling time required for a white dwarf to become a black dwarf exceeds the age of the Milky Way galaxy itself. Even if such a body did exist in orbit around the star, it would be massive enough that its gravitational attraction would cause the white dwarf to wobble noticeably as it orbited within the binary system every two hours or so. No such phenomenon had been found.

Interestingly, later observations of the star by Dr. James Graham of the California Institute of Technology showed very subtle 3- to 4-minute variations in its infrared output. Whatever was producing the infrared excess was also pulsating in brightness. While a pulsating brown dwarf is always a possibility, scientists began to wonder whether the source of the infrared excess was a ring of dust surrounding the star. The star Giclas 29-38 was already known to vary its brightness irregularly due to pulsations in its size and temperature. It seemed reasonable that circumstellar dust could absorb the varying amounts of starlight and emit variable infrared radiation in response.

Lacking any direct image of a companion object in orbit around the primary star, most astronomers argue in favor of a circumstellar dust cloud as the infrared source. Observations in 1992 revealed that the white dwarf star is apparently moving periodically toward and away from the Earth due to the gravitational influence of a companion object. Unfortunately, the source of the infrared emission from Giclas 29-38 remains a mystery.

A BROWN DWARF AT LAST?

Since his discovery of an infrared excess emanating from Giclas 29-38, Zuckerman has observed more than 120 white dwarf stars, finding at least 10 that radiate more infrared energy than expected. The most interesting of these is GD165. Its infrared excess is definitely caused by a companion object, GD165-B, and not by a dust cloud. The companion appears separated from the primary by nearly 18 billion kilometers. This is greater than the expanded atmosphere of the primary star during its red giant phase, thus ensuring that this companion could have survived unscathed. With a temperature of 2,100 Kelvin, GD165-B has become the coolest and dimmest brown dwarf candidate yet detected.

Astronomers have studied the spectrum of GD165-B to learn directly about its physical conditions and composition. At wavelengths from 1.5 to 2.5 microns, they found a very deep spectral absorption feature that is due to water vapor (steam) in the atmosphere of the star, a feature characteristic of the spectra of the lowest-mass stars, and which helps substantiate a brown dwarf interpretation. But to distinguish between a substellar brown dwarf and a low-mass red dwarf star—just as with Gliese 569-B—astronomers need to measure its mass. Unfortunately, the orbital period of this system is a few thousand years, and at least a full decade is needed to measure even a small amount of orbital motion.

So astronomers must, again, resort to theoretical models that relate mass to the luminosity and age of GD165-B. The result of this roundabout reasoning indicates a mass of about 75 Jupiter masses, right on the borderline between red and brown dwarfs. Although GD165-B may be the first confirmed brown dwarf in history, the evidence remains circumstantial until astronomers can make a definite measurement of its mass.

TRUSTY OL' ASTROMETRY

At the same time that Zuckerman and other astronomers were developing new techniques to search directly for the infrared emission from extrasolar planets, others were modifying existing techniques to do the same. George Gatewood, Director of the Allegheny Observatory in Pittsburgh, was putting an entirely new spin on the astrometric techniques made famous by Peter Van de Kamp decades earlier.

Van de Kamp used photographic plates taken months apart to search for wobbling motions of nearby stars from which he could infer the existence of invisible companions. But rather than using relatively sloppy photographic plates to search for wobbling stars, Gatewood developed a powerful new electronic detector to improve the accuracy of his measurements.

The seed of the idea was planted in Gatewood's mind during the presentation of a paper by SETI (Search for Extraterrestrial Intelligence) pioneer Frank Drake at the California Institute of

Technology. He suggested that one way of measuring precise stellar positions might be to let the Earth's rotation carry several stars past a slit in a detector and measure the exact times between their appearance and disappearance. Gatewood was so intrigued by Drake's talk that he conceived his detector overnight. "One morning, quite literally," he recalls, "I woke up, had the idea [for the new instrument], walked around the end of the bed, sat down at my desk, and was there until noon writing this thing down. I remember as I walked around the foot of the bed thinking, 'Well, it's not a perfect idea, but it'll have to do until something better comes along.' "

The device Gatewood had in mind was really quite simple. Instead of a slit, as Drake had suggested, it used a Ronchi ruling, a piece of glass with a number of fine lines scored on it. Each line, and the space between each line, is about as wide as a star image. Instead of letting a star drift across the field as in Drake's proposal, which meant that the technique was dependent on the Earth's rotation for part of the precision, the Ronchi ruling would be pulled across the starfield, causing the target stars to blink off and on and defining with remarkable precision the separation between them and, hence, their exact positions.

About six months later, Gatewood presented the idea for this device to his colleagues in another meeting at Cal Tech. After his talk, a man whom Gatewood did not recognize approached him, complimented him on the presentation, and asked how he intended to build the device. "Now at that point I didn't really intend to build [the thing]," recalls Gatewood. "I was there to tell *them* how to do it, and it kind of aggravated me a little with this 'let's get real here' sort of approach. So I sort of cut the conversation off as soon as I could and walked away. But I realized that I was going to have to build the darned thing when a friend said, 'I see that you were talking to [Nobel prize–winning physicist] Charlie Townes!'

"It was my realization that this man knew what he was talking about that led to my understanding," he continues. "An idea's cheap, you know. Everybody has ideas. The finished product—

the item that you're after—that's what's rare. That's what's of value. And I think that's what [Townes] was trying to tell me."

So Gatewood took the advice to heart and, with his observatory colleagues, began to build the device. "We did it in stages. Around 1978 [we built] what we called the 'IT,' or Image Trailer. It worked much like Frank Drake had suggested years before except that we used a ruling instead of a slit." Next, Gatewood added a computer to gather and analyze the data. "We were able to buy and build a small computer from Heathkit, [but] none of the people involved in this project knew any electronics. We taught ourselves by going down to Radio Shack, buying parts, taking them home, and making them smoke."

Upon completion, the device was installed and put to work on the Allegheny Observatory telescope. "We had a contest to see who could come up with the best name for it because we kept calling it 'the thing' out there," recalls Gatewood. "One of my graduate students came up with the name [we now use]: the Multichannel Astrometric Photometer, or MAP."

The MAP looks at twelve stars simultaneously through a Ronchi ruling that moves smoothly across the starfield. As it does, the lines pass across the star images, periodically blocking out light from each star. Light detectors positioned underneath each star then measure sinusoidal variations in light intensity versus time as the lines pass by. The relative timing between the twelve different sinusoids helps determine the relative separations between the stars. "It's a delightfully simple concept," says Gatewood. "That's what made it so darned hard to build. Simple concepts are always hard to implement."

Having built the MAP, Gatewood began his research by picking a target star and measuring its position relative to the eleven other stars in the field of view. By scanning the ruling back and forth for about an hour each night, a star's position can be measured with great precision—to within about 4 milliarc-seconds. Observations must then be repeated night after night to reveal the long-term effect of a star's orbital motion. Gatewood had learned long ago that measurements requiring such precision can be affected by tiny systematic errors so, as an added precaution, he added still another twist. Halfway through each night's observation, all the lenses and fiber optics that transfer light from each star to its respective light detector are reversed. Thus, everything that can be reversed on the starfield *is* reversed on the starfield, and systematic errors cannot creep into the data. Such attention to detail has paid off nicely for Gatewood. "We could never obtain that precision if we photographed a field for a whole year, measured all the plates, and took the average," he says.

From Gatewood's studies to date, nearly all of his stars show a straight line proper motion, with no telltale signs of unseen companions in orbit around them. But there's one star that stands out among all the others—the one that has "haunted" Gatewood since his earliest days as an astronomer. Its name is Barnard's Star. "Barnard's Star has the most interesting motion of all," says Gatewood. "It's going to be another year before I'm sure, but it doesn't seem to be going straight. Its the most distressful object to observe. It taxes your system to the limit so, if you find something, you're always worried about it. But I think we've got something." Whether it turns out to be the planetary companions announced by Van de Kamp decades ago remains to be seen.

A UNIQUE APPROACH

Another technique in the astronomer's arsenal has brought nearly full circle the ability to detect the presence of invisible companions by demonstrating gravitational tugging on the "parent" star. The method observes not the visible wobbling of a star's motion across the observer's line of sight, but the periodic variations of a star's motion toward and away from him. It uses the Doppler effect, discussed in Chapter 1.

When starlight passes through a prism or diffraction grating, its light is smeared into its constituent colors. When examined in detail, the resulting spectrum is crossed by a series of fine, dark lines—"holes" in the spectrum formed when various chemical elements and molecules in the atmospheres of stars absorb the light of specific colors before it escapes the star completely.

If a light source is stationary relative to an observer, its spectral lines will fall at predictable positions within the spectrum, positions that are determined by the atomic properties of the absorbing elements measured in Earth-based laboratories. For example, hydrogen can absorb light of a wavelength of 656 nanometers (6.56×10^{-7} meters), and always produces a dark line in the red portion of a star's spectrum. If, however, a star is moving toward an observer, the line would appear to be shifted slightly toward the blue end of the spectrum, and would appear to have a shorter wavelength. If the star is receding, its line would appear shifted toward the red end, and would be measured as having a longer wavelength. By comparing the positions of spectral lines of a star with those produced by a static reference light at the telescope itself, astronomers can measure the relative velocities of distant stars and galaxies anywhere in the universe.

This Doppler technique works only for stars whose motion carries them toward or away from an observer, so only a body's "radial" velocity can be detected by this technique. If a star seems to be oscillating toward *and* away from the Earth, astronomers might suspect the existence of an invisible companion—possibly even a planet—tugging on it in these directions as it orbits nearby. While this technique can produce such a discovery only indirectly, its unique advantages make it a very powerful tool.

Both techniques—astrometry and Doppler "accelerometry"—are nearly equal in their ability to detect a Jupiter-sized planet orbiting a solar-type star, but they do have their differences. Astrometry performs best on nearby stars because their motions across the sky appear greater, as well as on planets that might orbit a star in large orbits, again, because their angular motions are larger. Radial velocities, on the other hand, are limited by distance only because a great amount of light is needed to analyze a spectrum, and are more sensitive to short-period planets, which can produce greater velocity changes in the primary star. If astronomers could apply both techniques to the same stars, they could thoroughly analyze a planetary system since one is sensitive to outer bodies while the other is sensitive to inner bodies. Unfortunately, both methods involve long-term measurements because planets, if they exist at all, would require from one to hundreds of years to revolve around their parent stars.

Although the measurement of stellar radial velocities seems quite simple, in practice it is an entirely different matter. Typically, stellar velocity measurements provide accuracies of within about 3,200 kilometers per hour. Detecting the oscillating speed of a star caused by an orbiting planet is far more difficult. To detect a Jupiter-sized planet in orbit around another star would require a precision some thirty-five times greater—about 90 kilometers per hour. The technique to search for extrasolar planets with unprecedented accuracy was originally developed in the 1970s at the University of Arizona's Lunar and Planetary Laboratory by Krystof Serkowski.

Born in 1930, Serkowski emigrated from Poland in the 1960s and found work at the Lowell Observatory in Flagstaff, Arizona, before joining the staff of the University of Arizona in Tucson. He was an expert builder of scientific instruments and was talented at eliminating the bewildering variety of systematic errors that could influence high-precision research. In 1973, Serkowski learned that he was afflicted with amyotrophic lateral sclerosis (more commonly known as Lou Gehrig's disease) and was told he had only three years to live. The disease progressed much more slowly than doctors had predicted, however, and Serkowski remained intellectually active. His physical condition soon confined him to a wheelchair.

Eventually the physical deterioration became a serious handicap for him, and he became unable to conduct the lab's instrument development program and the search for extrasolar planets with his characteristic competence. So in 1979, Dr. Robert Mc-

Millan was hired to assist Serkowski with the project. In 1981 Serkowski died, and McMillan inherited the entire effort.

Why Serkowski began the search for other planets no one knows. "I'm not sure whether he chose to look for planets because of [his terminal disease] or not," says McMillan. "But he did say he thought it would help the overall problems of humanity if we could make contact with a more advanced and more sophisticated civilization. He wasn't a religious person, but I guess he really believed that this would be a better place if we could get some help from the outside."

Since installing his first instrument in September of 1985, Mc-Millan and his colleagues have visited their telescope a hundred nights each year, and are currently measuring the radial velocities of sixteen sunlike stars. "It's going to take a long time to find planets," concedes McMillan, "but the equipment's working well. We could use a little more money than we're actually getting, but I think we have one of the longest time series of radial velocity data at this level of accuracy."

Still, no planets have emerged from his data. Even if they had, McMillan would remain cautious. "If you look historically at all the claims for planet detection—all the misunderstandings and refutations through the years—there's really very little to be gained by premature announcements. If there is a planet orbiting one of these stars, that fact will become obvious to everybody observing it. It's not a good idea to jump the gun."

Perhaps most exciting for McMillan is the challenge of building the instruments to gather reliable data. "I'm trained as an astronomer, but somehow I prefer the company of engineers. To me it's an engineering challenge. It's very gratifying to see the equipment do what you designed it to do, and having the results come out reliably month after month, year after year. That's the real success. If there are planets out there, I can't be held responsible for that. My responsibility is to make sure that there are no spurious discoveries."

To assure achievement of that goal, McMillan has meticulously checked out every conceivable systematic error that could slip into his equipment. "The thing that's characteristic about announcements [of previous planet discoveries]," he explains, "is that the properties and limitations of the instrument were not published and described prior to the announcements." So Mc-Millan began observing objects other than his program stars to understand and calibrate his equipment thoroughly—objects for which the radial velocities are already well known. These included special emission line lamps in the laboratory where the relative velocity should be zero, as well as sunlight reflecting off of a crater on the moon to simulate observations of stars like the sun. Unlike individual stars, the moon is available at all seasons of the year, and thus provides many opportunities to learn how well the instrument really works.

Determining if the radial velocity oscillations that McMillan's team is observing are caused by unseen planetary companions in orbit around other stars will take many years of research. But McMillan is a relatively young man, and has all the time in the world to wait it out. "I think it would bother me if I were twenty years older and starting this," he explained. "It's not that much different from anybody else's scientific career. We do other stuff with the instrument: we study variable stars and stellar pulsations, we've found variations in stars with periods anywhere from three hours to several years, and we've already discovered three new types of variations in [certain types of] giant stars. It's a regular, on-going active research program. It's not like we're just grinding along and one answer comes along in the end thirty years later."

There is, however, one very difficult aspect of such a long-term science project: trying to sell it to a sponsor and receive telescope time. As a member of the University of Arizona's telescope allocation committee for three years, McMillan has seen it all too clearly. "Because money and telescope time is so heavily oversubscribed," he explains, "there's a tendency for investigators to do what I call 'safe science': a very minute experiment is described in which there are only one of two possible outcomes and, in both cases, the investigator expects to have a significant paper to write. Scientists are packaging their research into these palatable little safe increments so that people were not feeling like they're buying into any kind of a risky venture. I think that everybody who's trying to look for planets has faced this to a certain extent. It's not so much the time scale as it is the general skepticism in the scientific community that such a thing can even be done."

PLANETS BY SERENDIPITY

While McMillan and his colleagues were consciously searching for the existence of extrasolar planets, others did so inadvertently.

Throughout the 1980s, astronomers at the Oak Ridge Observatory at Harvard University were busy calibrating their new fiber-optic spectrograph. For seven years, Smithsonian astronomer Dr. David Latham and his colleagues had monitored the radial velocity of the star HD114762, a faint, sunlike star 80 light-years from Earth in the constellation of Coma Berenices, for use as a calibration standard. Then in August of 1988, the astronomers announced their results.

The star was not the constant "standard" that they had expected. Instead, it appeared to be wobbling toward and away from the Earth over a period of 84.2 days, and the astronomers had observed the star's motion through no less than thirty orbital cycles. Although obviously unsuitable as a calibration standard, the star's companion provided a remarkable candidate for a brown dwarf or extrasolar planet. In fact, the investigators theorized that the wobble is caused by an object orbiting as close to the star as Mercury does to the sun.

Latham and his colleagues now suspect that the object causing the wobble may weigh as much as 10 Jupiters, but no one knows for sure. Whether the object is a planet, a brown dwarf, or a small star remains a mystery. This is because the tilt of its orbit cannot be determined. If the object is orbiting its star in a direction along their direct line of sight (in other words, in and out of the plane of the sky), then the astronomers have measured the full amount of the star's wobble and can estimate the companion's mass accurately. But if the object orbits at right angles to their line of sight (i.e., within the plane of the sky), then the measurements do not represent the full wobble and the companion could be substantially larger—or even closer to its parent star—than they believe.

Nevertheless, astronomers were quite excited about this find. "This is certainly the most convincing evidence so far for a low-mass companion around another star," said Latham, echoing a familiar theme. A promising candidate indeed, but still not a sure thing.

OTHERS AT WORK

As sensitive as these new techniques were for measuring the radial velocities of stars, they could still be improved. Two Canadian astronomers, Drs. Bruce Campbell and Gordon Walker, set out to do even better.

Campbell and Walker recognized that conventional Doppler radial velocity measurements, in which one measures the wavelength of an absorption line in the spectrum of a star and then compares it with the wavelength of light produced by an emission line source within the telescope itself, can introduce serious problems. Since the star beam and the lamp beam may not travel through the spectrograph in exactly the same way, they reasoned, systematic errors could easily appear. "It's as though the ruler against which you're measuring wavelengths—the standard ruler—is shifted by an arbitrarily small amount," explains Campbell, "and it leaves you with an error of measurement of typically a thousand meters per second. Conventional techniques can do nothing about this; there's simply no way to get rid of this error. You can measure a given star thousands of times and beat the error down that way, but still there's this inherent problem of measurement."

For detecting something as tiny as the reflex motion of stars due to orbiting planets, this just wouldn't do. So, instead of relying on a separate lamp to generate a stationary comparison spectrum, Campbell passed the light from his target stars through a tube of hydrogen fluoride before it entered the spectrograph. The gas absorbed light of specific colors and "imprinted" onto the star's actual spectrum a static set of lines that could be used as reference wavelengths.

Hydrogen fluoride is an extremely noxious and dangerous gas, but no other could provide what Campbell and Walker needed, since it exhibits an extremely simple spectrum with relatively few, nicely separated, yet easily measured absorption lines. The astronomers simply adopted common laboratory safety procedures, such as exhausting air from the vicinity of the equipment, enclosing it in a Plexiglas container, and exercising extreme caution when handling the equipment.

Not only is hydrogen fluoride harmful to the human body, it also is harmful to glass, putting the optics in the vicinity of the equipment at risk. "Some would say that's even worse than the hazard to the astronomers," quips Campbell. To avoid this problem, the astronomers designed a special container to hold the gas safely. "It's a long tube made of special metal that's inert to hydrogen fluoride gas. The windows on the ends are made of another inert material—sapphire. They're rather expensive windows!"

When applied to the heavens, the astronomers found that their new "precision radial velocity" technique reduced the errors inherent in previous methods by nearly a hundred times, allowing them to measure velocities of stars as small as about 13 meters per second—roughly the speed of an Olympic sprinter. This accuracy would be sufficient to reveal the gravitational pull of Jupiter on a star like the sun.

The beginnings of the project were rather simple. "The first experiment Bruce and I did was before Christmas 1976," recalls Walker. "Bruce put the whole thing together, and it was pretty jerry-rigged. We used it one afternoon looking at the sun in Victoria (British Columbia). The results turned out very well and showed that, basically, the technique worked. Then Bruce got money to build the hydrogen fluoride cell and the gas-handling system which he developed, and we [added] the detector that we developed for the Canada-France-Hawaii Telescope." When they checked it all out at the telescope, it was still less than a high-tech effort but, as Walker summarizes, "it worked."

An important contributor to the experiment's success was an electronic detector known as a silicon photodiode array. Its extreme sensitivity to small amounts of light helped measure the positions of spectral lines to a precision unheard of in conventional astronomical spectroscopy. Using this detector attached to the 3.6-meter Canada-France-Hawaii Telescope on Mauna Kea, the scientists began their ten-year project in 1980. Their goal was to study some two dozen nearby sunlike stars for periodic velocity variations that might suggest the presence of planetary or brown dwarf companions orbiting nearby.

Campbell was optimistic from the beginning. "We had no idea whether it would actually work, but we thought, 'Let's go for it anyway.' There are lots of things you can measure with such velocity precision," he says, "but this was the project to go after, even though it would take a very long time."

Campbell and Walker not only had a unique capability, they also had good timing. Of the three groups of U.S. researchers who had also developed high-precision radial velocity techniques, none was yet performing actual observations. The Canadians had a five-year head start. In searching for Jupiter-like planets orbiting sunlike stars, at least a dozen years are required to observe a single orbital revolution, so the other groups could not possibly catch up to the Canadians' lead.

To select their target stars, Campbell and Walker considered some very special criteria. The stars needed to be bright enough so that the narrow spectral lines would be easily measurable. For example, a star of fourth magnitude (6.3 times brighter than the naked eye limit) requires 30 minutes to measure. According to Campbell: "It's very unusual to use a large telescope to observe stars you can see with the naked eye. That's something that people have remarked about many times."

They also decided to concentrate on stars similar to the sun. Stars that were hotter would not produce spectral lines in the region where the hydrogen fluoride lines appear. They excluded many giant stars from consideration because of concerns that convection motions within the stars' atmospheres would produce their own radial velocity effects, and possibly mimic those produced by an orbiting planet. A final criterion was that the stars should not be known binaries; otherwise, radial velocity variations from the known companion star would appear in the data.

For six years, Campbell and Walker measured the spectra of their program stars. Then, in 1986, when they first looked at the results of their study, they got a surprise. Approximately half the stars showed some kind of long-term variation in velocity: either a straight line change or a curving trend that seemed to be a small portion of a long-term period.

They explored a number of different phenomena that could have contributed to such velocity variations in the stars: expansion and contraction of the stars themselves; starspots rotating periodically into view; large convective bubbles rising and sinking in the stars' atmospheres. None could explain the variations they recorded. In the absence of any other plausible origin, the astronomers proposed that the data must represent the wobbling motion of the stars caused by the gravitational tug by unseen companion bodies. Their preliminary calculations suggested that some of these companions could be as small as Jupiter, but at least a decade or two will be required to measure a complete orbit and confirm the exact nature of the companion bodies.

One of the most intriguing of their finds was a star known as Gamma Cephei, a known binary system in the constellation of Cepheus. The radial velocity data for this star system clearly revealed both a long-term trend, caused by the widely separated companion star, and a much shorter, two-and-a-half-year variation apparently caused by another companion with nearly the mass of Jupiter, but in a Mars-sized orbit. Unfortunately, Gamma Cephei is a subgiant star, and what looks like a straight periodicity may, in fact, be due to instabilities within the star itself. Only more observations will reveal the true story. However, if the companion proves to be real, it would be the first planetary body found orbiting within a binary star system—something, until recently, thought to be impossible.

For Campbell, it was all his dreams come true. "All through this, I kept having to pinch myself, because it didn't seem right that we should be so lucky," he says. "We started out with this new technique, and were lucky enough to have probably the only telescope in the world capable of doing [this project]. And we were lucky getting all that telescope time; frequently it's tough to get one night, let alone six nights, a year."

But Campbell's dream work would not last long. While conducting his successful research at the University of British Columbia and at Victoria University, funding ran out and his position was terminated. And no amount of bureaucratic cajoling and maneuvering could save it. After six months, according to Campbell, "I couldn't see myself waiting around for some other opportunity. I had simply reached the breaking point, and I had to back away from the situation as far as I could." He retreated from astronomy and the search for extrasolar planets and is now successful in his own business, with little likelihood of ever returning.

The program he began, however, continues under the direction of Walker. One of his priorities has been to reduce the errors inherent in the technique to about 10 meters per second in order to reveal more subtle variations in radial velocities corresponding to either smaller planets or those moving more slowly in large orbits. His plan is to accomplish these improvements while continuing to accumulate a long time base of measurements on the stars already observed.

VARIATIONS ON A THEME

Another astronomer has also pursued the measurement of stellar radial velocities using an absorption cell. However, in contrast to the hydrogen fluoride cell used by Campbell and Walker, Dr. William Cochran of the University of Texas employs iodine. Cochran became interested in high-precision radial velocities as a postdoc, while trying to measure wind speeds in the atmosphere of Venus. This experience led him unexpectedly into the field of extrasolar planetary detection.

The technique he began with was quite different, and had first been suggested by Roger Griffin of Cambridge University. The idea was that relatively high precision radial velocities could be measured easily, simply by taking a spectrum of a star in a spectral region in which the Earth's atmosphere provides some narrow absorption lines. He had suggested that there is a molecular oxygen band near the wavelength of 630 nanometers that provides a prominent set of fairly narrow, well-spaced absorption lines. This idea works because a strong wavelength reference system is imposed on the star's spectrum before it goes into the spectrograph. Any optical effects that are imposed by the spectrograph will influence both the stellar spectrum and the reference spectrum and, therefore, to a first order should cancel out.

Under ideal circumstances, precisions of 10 meters per second are possible with this technique. However, conditions are not always ideal since the Earth's atmosphere is not a stable environment, and the reference lines show radial velocity fluctuations during windy periods. So, following the methods used by Campbell and Walker, Cochran decided to find a suitable gas to use in an absorption cell. He chose iodine and began his work.

Cochran has obtained some interesting results on the star HD114762, which, as discovered earlier, was announced to be a radial velocity variable by David Latham. Cochran had been observing this star even before Latham's announcement, and became especially interested in determining the inclination angle of the companion's orbit in this system. You may recall that the mass of the companion depends critically on this angle, and it is crucial in determining whether the companion is stellar or substellar in nature.

Cochran and his colleagues began trying to determine the inclination angle by assuming that the companion's orbit might have an axis aligned with the rotational axis of the primary star. They would then examine the stellar spectral lines of the primary to determine the tilt of its axis. In this process, they learned that either the star was not rotating—which, in itself, would be an astounding situation—or they were looking right down the star's rotational axis. Unfortunately, this meant that the companion object was most likely not substellar, because its true velocity was actually much higher than the measured radial velocity due to the tilt of the system. "It's a disappointing result," he concluded.

On his other results Cochran is mum. However, he admits that some stars are displaying radial velocity variations, and that his research group is analyzing whether something strange is occurring in their instrument, or if there really is something there.

Like McMillan, Cochran also feels the competition for funding. "NASA feels that planet detection is a very important area of research. The amount of funds available never keeps up with inflation and the growth of the number of people competing for those funds. So there's always competition for funding. The argument I try to use is that we need at least two programs operating out there because, in any sort of science, the result you get must be repeatable. And it must be verifiable through independent methods."

Trying to get funding for a long-term research project is, perhaps, even tougher. "It's very difficult to go to an agency like NASA or the National Science Foundation and say, 'Look, I'm doing this wonderful important research. Please give me a significant amount of money and I'll give you the answer in ten years,' " says Cochran. "They tend to look askance at that. So, of course, you try to generate interim results along the way—

to keep them interested—to convince them that you really are doing frontline work and that you're not just taking money and squandering it. That's why the result on HD114762 is not only an interesting result, but it's also crucial to the problem of maintaining funding."

There's another form of competition going on as well—competition on a more human level. "There's always this danger that one wants to be first," says Walker. "Frankly, I think that our program got a little too much publicity in the past, and that may have raised expectations. I was never totally thrilled about the limelight when we had it, because we just simply needed time to consolidate what we had. I don't think we ever made any claims we couldn't support. They tend to get blown out of proportion."

Cochran agrees. "Of course, if there's a signal in one of these stars, each one of us wants to be the first one coming out with it because, as you know, the first person to detect something gets all the credit. You don't really remember the second person to do anything. Sure we're out here for the intellectual activity, but we're also trying to discover something. And we do want to get credit for what we do."

SPECKLE IMAGING SURVEYS

While McMillan, Campbell, Walker, and Cochran were pursuing radial velocity measurements in search of planetary companions, still other astronomers were searching for the direct infrared emission from warm brown dwarf companions around nearby stars. Using the same speckle methods used in Mc-Carthy's observations of VB8, two research groups employed more modern infrared detectors to enable the detection of much fainter companions.

The first group involved Todd Henry, a graduate student working with McCarthy at the University of Arizona. Henry's idea was to survey systematically red dwarf stars for evidence of companions. Red dwarfs were chosen because potential brown dwarf companions would not be lost in the glare of the primary star and because they would lie at wider separations than around more massive stars. Henry and McCarthy observed all seventy-four red dwarfs located within 26 light-years of the sun that were observable from the Northern Hemisphere.

The new infrared detector gave these astronomers the ability to detect unambiguously any brown dwarfs with masses larger than about 50 Jupiters. Although six new companions were discovered, none were shown to be definitely substellar. The results, published in 1991, clearly demonstrated that any substellar companions must be either extremely faint or nonexistent. Clearly, there appeared a dramatic drop in the number of companion objects just as one passes from the mass regime of the red dwarf stars into that of the brown dwarfs. The separate survey of white dwarf stars by Zuckerman and Becklin also reached the same conclusion. Thus, it seems that there are very few brown dwarf companions to be found.

Why would nature stop making objects right at the dividing line between brown dwarfs and red dwarf stars? No one has yet proposed how to relate the theory of star formation to that of nuclear burning inside of stars in a way that would predict why bodies should stop forming at exactly the mass where nuclear fusion ceases. Possibly, the theoretical predictions of the luminosity of bright brown dwarfs were overestimates. Henry and McCarthy are expanding their sensitivity with yet another, more sensitive infrared detector to examine this possibility.

At the same time, another graduate student researcher, Andrea Ghez of the California Institute of Technology, was using the same speckle techniques to search for companions among young T Tauri stars in the star-forming regions of Taurus-Auriga and Ophiuchus-Scorpius. Recall that T Tauri stars are thought to be extremely young stars like the sun. Ghez used the Hale 5-meter telescope on Palomar Mountain to achieve the high resolution needed to see close companions at the relatively large distances of these regions—nearly 500 light-years.

In her 1992 Ph.D. thesis, Ghez reported a surprisingly large proportion of companions among these young stars. She concluded that at least 60 percent of the T Tauri stars were binaries—a factor of four greater than the older solar-type stars. The implication was that "most, if not all, T Tauri stars have companions."

Ghez's study raises many fundamental questions. Why is the sun single instead of part of a binary system? Was it at one time part of a binary system that was somehow disrupted? Is the solar system really the result of the formation of a single star? By excluding known binary stars from their searches, are astronomers looking for planetary systems in the wrong places? Could planetary systems like our own really be rare and, if so, are astronomers biasing their searches by searching for such rarities?

No one knows the answers to these questions. Good research always seems to generate more and more questions, while providing new insight.

A CONFUSING SITUATION?

In recent years, many astronomers have joined the search for other planetary systems using the most modern technological tools and creative observing techniques. Yet, despite this effort no one has yet proved convincingly the discovery of a single planet or brown dwarf orbiting another star. Does this mean that there are no other planets orbiting other stars—that no other worlds exist beyond those of our own solar system? Most scientists think not.

Instead, it may be that technology has not yet provided the capabilities needed to detect them. That may soon be changing, as the search for other solar systems assumes an even higher priority among astronomers. The future of the search looks bright, as larger and larger ground-based telescopes are being built, and as space-based telescopes and interferometers begin to be used to observe the heavens from Earth-orbit and, possibly, from the moon.

✳ The W. M. Keck Observatory at the summit of Mauna Kea is currently the world's largest optical telescope. With a segmented-mirror diameter of 10 meters, this instrument can gather four times more light than the Hale Reflector at Palomar Observatory near San Diego.

✳ An artist's conception illustrates the ring of dusty material in orbit around the bright star Vega, discovered by the Infrared Astronomical Satellite (IRAS) in 1983. The ring is thin enough to allow the light from more distant stars to shine through. The plane of the Milky Way appears to the right.

Photo: NASA

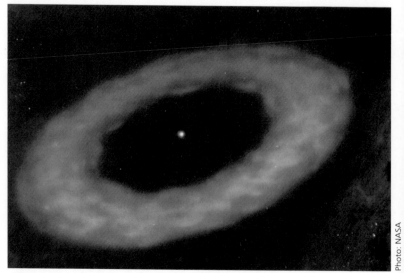

Photo: NASA

✳ This edge-on disk was photographed in 1984 by astronomers Brad Smith and Richard Terrile using a tiny mask to block the starlight from Beta Pictoris. The disk turned out to be ten times larger than our own solar system, and nearly three times larger than the disk found around Vega one year earlier.

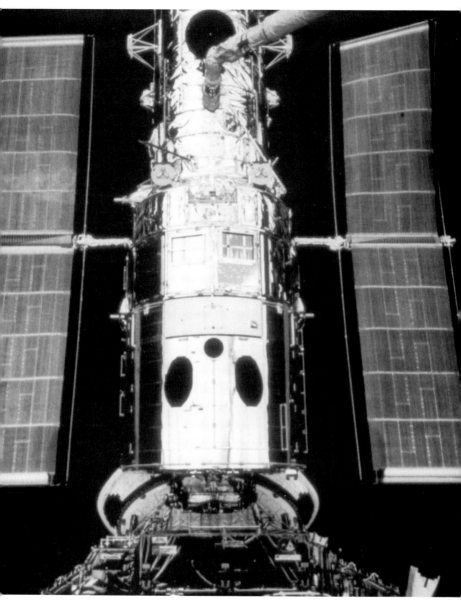

✳ During its first servicing mission in 1990, the Hubble Telescope is held in the cargo bay of *Endeavour* by the space shuttle's remote manipulator arm. The two giant solar panels from which the telescope draws its electrical power are seen flanking the telescope's optical tube.

Photo: NASA

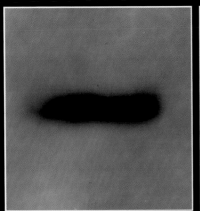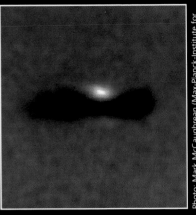

✴ An embryonic planetary system is seen deep within the clouds of the Orion Nebula. With a diameter about 17 times that of our own solar system, this is the largest of several recently found within the nebula. The left image is a composite of blue, green, and red light, and the right image was shot through a filter that blocks bright emissions from the background nebula.

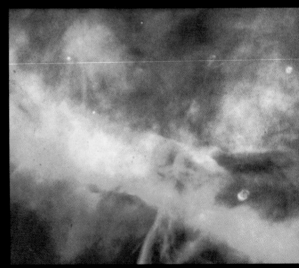

✴ One of the nearest "stellar nurseries" is the Great Orion Nebula, 1,500 light-years from Earth. This giant cloud is illuminated by the brightest of the young hot stars at the top right of this 1993 Hubble Telescope photo. Tiny spherical clumps near the center are believed to be planetary systems in the process of formation.

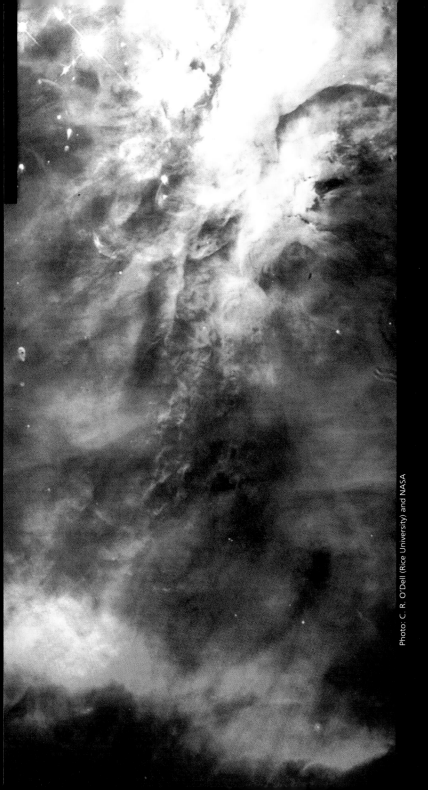

Photo: Robert Williams and the Hubble Deep Field Team (STScI and NASA)

✳ Several hundred never-before-seen galaxies are visible in this "deepest-ever" view of the universe, shot by the Hubble Space Telescope in December 1995. This image covers an area of the sky only 1/30 of the full moon's diameter, or the equivalent area to that blocked out by a grain of sand held at arm's length!

❋ Since the *Voyager* spacecraft will leave the Solar System and journey outward on a multimillion-year trek to the stars, scientists attached to its body a gold-plated phonograph record, complete with cartridge and stylus. Called *Sounds of Earth*, this interstellar postcard features messages from five dozen world leaders, geological and biological sounds, music, and images to capture the essence of light on planet Earth. It is expected to last a billion years.

❋ Out of swirling clouds of dust and gas planets like Earth almost certainly evolve. The only world we know for sure to contain life of any kind is shown in this spectacular *Apollo* 17 photograph. The entire continent of Africa can be seen to the upper left, and the huge white mass at the bottom is Antarctica.

PLANETS AROUND NORMAL STARS

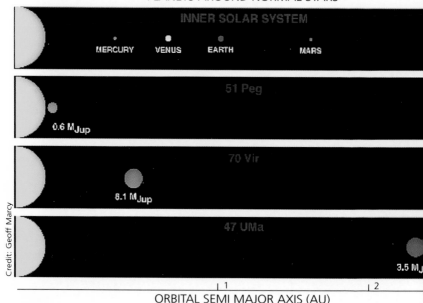

ORBITAL SEMI MAJOR AXIS (AU)

Credit: Geoff Marcy

✳ **THE LATEST DISCOVERIES!** In January 1996, Drs. Geoff Marcy and Paul Butler (San Francisco State University) announced planets orbiting the solar-type stars 70 Virginis and 47 Ursae Majoris. This graphic compares the three known extrasolar planetary systems to our own inner solar system *(top panel)*. Whereas 51 Pegasi B *(second panel)* is less massive than Jupiter and revolves every 4.2 days in a very small circular orbit,

70 Virginis B *(third panel)* has a mass of around 8 Jupiters and a larger elliptical orbit with a period of 117 days. The Virginis "super-planet" thus resembles the companion to HD114762 and is likely a small brown dwarf. The bottom panel shows 47 Ursae Majoris B, a planet about three times more massive than Jupiter, revolving in a circular orbit nearly twice the size of our Earth's orbit, with a period of about three years.

✳ Peter Van de Kamp of Swarthmore College in Pennsylvania was the first astronomer ever to announce the detection of planets in orbit around another sun. His work on Barnard's Star spanned many decades and inspired the work of several generations of modern astronomers.

Photo: Swarthmore College

7

THE SEARCH CONTINUES

From the multitude of discoveries made in recent years, it is clear that ours is a special time in history—a time when humans can finally begin to answer fundamental questions about the uniqueness of our planetary home and of ourselves. However, because some of these "discoveries" have not been confirmed (and some even refuted!), it is also clear that technologies and techniques are in need of a breakthrough. This new planetary awareness has prompted scientists to consider developing a formal program to discover and examine planetary systems around other stars.

In 1990, after a series of scientific workshops and committee studies, the National Research Council's Committee on Planetary and Lunar Exploration (COMPLEX) published a report entitled *Strategy for the Detection and Study of Other Planetary Systems and Extrasolar Planetary Materials*. This report recognized that technology is now "on the brink of major advances," and that science would be able to learn within only a few decades whether or not the solar system is one of many. However, the report also recognized the significant technical challenges that lie ahead, and they recommended that NASA undertake "a major scientific effort" to scrutinize the heavens in search of other planets and planetary systems.

It might, at first, seem odd that NASA would be interested in finding planets and planetary systems around other stars, since the tremendous distances to these worlds would all but prohibit direct exploration. The reasons for this effort are outlined by Dr. Wes Huntress, Chief of NASA's Solar System Exploration Division. "It's important to understand how planets form. We have plenty of examples of them in our own solar system but, in fact, are we unique? Each of those answers has some very profound conclusions one can draw from them. So, to the extent that one of NASA's primary goals is to understand the formation and evolution of our solar system, it's important to know if there are other examples. Besides, who's to say that we won't be able to visit them at some point in our history?"

TOWARD OTHER PLANETARY SYSTEMS

In 1990, in response to the recommendations of COMPLEX, NASA began a three-phase program called TOPS (Toward Other Planetary Systems) to discover extrasolar planetary systems and to characterize their formation processes. "The TOPS program, therefore, represents an expansion of NASA's horizon outward beyond Neptune and Pluto," explains Huntress. "It would progress systematically, beginning with a ground-based program of research, [expanding] to the use of orbital platforms and, finally, to either a major observatory-class platform in Earth-orbit or on the lunar surface."

The first phase (TOPS-0) is already underway. With an immediate goal of developing the means to detect planetary masses as small as that of Uranus and Neptune in orbit around 100 or more stars, this phase encourages the continuation of the direct and indirect detection methods described earlier. However, these methods will be improved considerably through the use of much larger telescopes and more sensitive electronic detectors, and with the implementation of new techniques to overcome atmospheric blurring.

Another key component of TOPS-0 is to prepare for the program's second phase (TOPS-1), scheduled to begin at the end of this century, which will feature a special Earth-orbiting observatory. Three instruments are now under consideration: the Orbiting Stellar Interferometer (OSI), the Precision Optical Interferometer in Space (POINTS), and the Astrometric Imaging Telescope (AIT).

The third, and possibly final, phase (TOPS-2) would involve a major observatory–class telescope in high Earth-orbit or on the surface of the moon. This facility would be capable both of detecting Earth-like planets and of characterizing their physical and chemical properties.

The scale of the TOPS program is enormous and, despite their excitement about their plans, scientists recognize that such a major expenditure of money and resources will require a significant national or international commitment. "The whole question of other worlds around other stars," says Dr. Robert Brown, of the Space Telescope Science Institute and a member of the TOPS team, "is something that might well be articulated by a president or vice president who wanted to state a truly outstanding scientific goal that everyone could understand, and one that would have an answer. And this might be done in the context of a colony on the moon."

Despite the years of bureaucratic scrutiny the plan will have to endure, Huntress is confident that it will hold up. "It's a phased program that builds systematically toward some very capable hardware [that will] not only detect planets, but study their atmospheres and planetary disks around other stars in order to understand the process of solar system formation.

"There's a strong science program of observations, laboratory, and theoretical work that would go along with it," he continues. "So it's intended to be a very well-rounded, totally encompassing campaign to try to address this issue, because I think that the unambiguous detection of another planet around another star has got to be a major fundamental discovery in our times. It'll change the way in which we think about ourselves on our little planet."

SPECIAL-PURPOSE GROUND-BASED TELESCOPES

As part of the TOPS plan of improving astronomers' ability to detect extrasolar planets by way of astrometric and radial velocity techniques, new telescopes have been proposed for performing long-term observational work.

The first is called the Astrometric Technology Telescope, or ATT. It would feature an improved version of George Gatewood's Multichannel Astrometric Photometer (MAP) attached to the focus of a 1.5-meter telescope. With this instrument, astrometric precision would be improved by 300 percent over currently used techniques, and Gatewood believes that the ATT would be capable of studying about 100 stars accurately enough to discover a Jupiter-like planet in orbit around them—possibly even something as small as Saturn.

While Gatewood is optimistic about the success of this telescope in the search for extrasolar planets, he recognizes that its construction may be years away. "It's a proposal that's been kicking around for a while," he explains. "NSF [the National Science Foundation] and NASA have heard about it, and they've indicated an interest in supporting it, at least on a partial level. But every time we get ready to go in [with a proposal], there's a funding crisis and we say, 'Well, maybe we'll wait until next year.' So that's sort of where it hangs right now."

Another telescope, this one designed for use with the radial velocity detection method, is already under construction in Texas. William Cochran has been using the 2.7-meter telescope of the McDonald Observatory in West Texas to search the spectra of thirty-three distant stars for Doppler shifts that suggest the presence of orbiting planets. "But to address the real scientific questions here," he explains, "we need a much larger sample.

In fact, I'd like to have a hundred or two hundred stars, but I can't just add more stars to the list because there aren't any that are bright enough. As I get down to fainter and fainter stars, I can't get the precision that's necessary."

The solution to this problem is a collaborative effort between the University of Texas, the Pennsylvania State University, and three other partners to construct a large telescope whose sole purpose is spectroscopy. When completed in 1996, this $13 million behemoth will feature an array of eighty-five 1-meter-diameter circular mirrors joined together on a single dish, providing the light-collecting power of a single 8.5-meter-diameter mirror. Its simple mounting will not allow the telescope to operate in a conventional sense. Instead, the telescope will be constantly aimed 70 degrees above the horizon, and its base will rotate in azimuth (around the horizon) to pick up targets as they cross the sky at that altitude, enabling the telescope to view 70 percent of the West Texas sky.

GROUND-BASED SUPERSCOPES

The next step in finding extrasolar planets and planetary systems from Earth is to build larger telescopes that will collect more light and focus it more precisely to provide the highest possible resolution. For nearly half a century, the largest and most powerful telescope in the world has been the 5-meter-diameter Hale reflector on Palomar Mountain in southern California. However, to find and study extrasolar planets, much larger telescopes will be needed—to pierce the shrouds of dust around protostars for a possible first glimpse of planetary birth, to record the very faint images of other worlds, and, from their light, to measure the bodies' temperatures, brightnesses, and chemical compositions.

Constructing a telescope larger than the Hale reflector is not particularly easy or inexpensive; that telescope required more than a decade of design and construction. Its primary mirror required more than a year to cool from its molten state before engineers could begin to grind out its curved shape. Although astronomers and engineers in the Soviet Union succeeded in constructing a telescope 1 meter larger in diameter, they have yet to make the light it gathers come to an ideal focus.

With a telescope mirror twice the diameter of the Hale primary mirror, four times more light would be focused into an image four times smaller in area, so that stars sixteen times fainter could be detected. However, using conventional manufacturing technology, this mirror would be about eight times heavier, and the final telescope would cost at least eight times more. Even if the expense were not prohibitive, the sheer weight of the mirror would cause its surface to sag, blurring the focused image. In addition, this large mass of glass would never reach thermal equilibrium with the nighttime air, producing small air currents above it that would further blur the final image.

If astronomers ever hope to find planets and planetary systems in orbit around distant stars, a totally new telescope technology—a radical new idea and design—is needed. In fact, three new technologies are now being applied to the construction of new telescope mirrors.

One such technology is already in operation on a 4,270-meter-high peak of an extinct Hawaiian volcano known as Mauna Kea. The Keck telescope, the newest in a new generation of superscopes, features a primary mirror nearly 10 meters across. This $94 million colossus was built by a partnership between the California Institute of Technology and the University of California, and was funded primarily by a $70 million grant from the W. M. Keck Foundation—the largest private contribution ever for a scientific project.

What makes Keck unique is that its 10-meter mirror is not a single piece of glass. It is built instead of thirty-six 2-meter-wide segments, each less than 8 centimeters thick, packed closely together in a honeycomb arrangement. Because the individual mirror segments are so much thinner than a monolithic 10-meter mirror, the telescope requires only one-third as much glass and weighs less than half that of its smaller Palomar cousin. Also, with a height of only 24.6 meters, Keck fits neatly into a dome the size of the Hale reflector.

Since Keck's mirror is not composed of a single optical surface, electronic control systems must continuously monitor the alignment of each segment and make adjustments to the mirror's overall shape. Otherwise, the light it gathers would not be focused as finely as possible. To do this, an intricate network of sensors monitors the position of each segment and relays this data to a central computer. Twice each second, the computer sends commands to an array of motorized actuators that nudge each segment by less than 3×10^5 millimeters to keep the incoming light focused at a point.

Another new technology for making large telescopes produces monolithic mirrors that are hollow or "honeycombed" inside. Up to 8.4 meters in diameter, these mirrors are manufactured at the University of Arizona's Mirror Lab using a spin-casting method applied to the same kind of glass used in Pyrex cookware. In this technique, molten glass in a furnace is spun, allowing centrifugal force to produce in the molten glass a concave shape.

The idea for this project arose several years ago in response to the tremendous need for lightweight, low-cost, and short-focus mirrors. Hollow mirrors had been first used successfully in the late 1970s on the Multiple-Mirror Telescope (MMT) on Mt. Hopkins in southern Arizona. Because these mirrors could cool quickly to the nighttime air temperature, this telescope provided vastly improved image quality over previous generations of instruments. Realizing the advantages offered by mirrors with a honeycombed interior, University of Arizona astronomer Dr. Roger Angel began experimenting with a homemade furnace. Now, as director of the UA's Mirror Lab, Angel has overseen the casting and polishing of mirrors as large as 6.5 meters and is now planning the construction of an 8.4-meter mirror.

Instead of following traditional casting methods, where glass is melted, poured into a mold, cooled, and then ground to shape, Angel's team does it all in one step. Pieces of borosilicate glass

(Pyrex) are carefully piled on a mold in the center of the furnace and heated to 1,200 degrees Celsius. As the molten glass settles into the ribbed mold, a honeycomb structure of the blank is created. When the pieces are melted completely, the turntable begins spinning, creating a curved surface of molten glass inside the furnace. The furnace lid is then lifted, slowly dropping the inside temperature as the turntable continues spinning and the glass solidifies.

After the mirror's casting is complete, a computer-controlled polishing machine then smoothes its surface to 3×10^5 millimeters. The curvature given to such mirrors is a major advantage as well. A steeply curved ("fast") mirror featuring a short focal length focuses starlight at a point relatively close to the mirror's surface. This enables the telescope tube to be short, and the structure housing the instrument to be smaller and less expensive.

The final result is a continuous, curved surface of glass atop a lightweight honeycomb base. The stability of this base maintains the mirror's correct shape and produces well-focused images. Furthermore, the entire casting process takes only a few months, compared to several years with traditional methods.

A third technology for constructing future telescope mirrors is now being developed by both the Schott Glassworks and Corning. It is called the thin meniscus (or constant thickness) mirror. These mirrors, too, are spuncast, but are so thin and frail that astronomers and engineers must rely on computer-controlled actuators attached to their undersides to flex the glass surface to the proper curvature. This technology has been adopted for the proposed 8-meter-diameter telescopes planned by European and Japanese astronomers.

By the end of the decade, perhaps a dozen or more 8-meter instruments will be aimed skyward in search of circumstellar disks, brown dwarfs, and extrasolar planets. Telescopes fitted with such mirrors may eventually produce images sharp enough to detect extrasolar planets. These would be due not entirely to the mirrors themselves, but also to the attached instrumentation that examines the images created by the mirror.

INSTRUMENTATION FOR GROUND-BASED TELESCOPES

What excites planet hunters, at least as much as the huge aperture of the Keck telescope itself, is the array of electronic gadgetry that makes it efficient.

One of the greatest impacts on modern astronomy has come from the development of electronic light detectors. Charge-coupled devices, or CCDs, essentially convert light into electrons, which can be collected, counted, and converted in a computer, first into numbers and then into colors. For the past decade or so, CCDs have been incorporated into cameras, spectrographs, and other light-gathering instruments, and have effectively multiplied the sensitivity of existing telescopes to both visible and infrared light by hundreds or thousands of times. With detector arrays of more than 4 million picture elements (or pixels) in each chip, CCDs produce images comparable in quality to those achieved by standard photographic techniques, yet with much shorter exposure times.

For example, modern infrared cameras employ electronic detectors with up to 1 million pixels, each of which by itself is more efficient than the individual detectors used at Palomar in the late 1980s. Continuing improvements are being made in both the number of individual pixels available and in the performance of each one, such that it is now possible for a single infrared pixel to respond to a power level of one-millionth of one-billionth of 1 watt.

Other powerful technologies are also being developed to revolutionize ground-based astronomy and improve the chances of finding planets of other stars. Ironically, many of these are the result of new applications from original military research. Some can even remove the blurring distortions produced as starlight travels through Earth's turbulent atmosphere.

At even the finest observing sites on Earth, atmospheric distortion prevents astronomers from seeing details smaller than about 0.5 arc second across. This distortion—known to astronomers as "seeing"—arises when turbulent pockets of air above the telescope bend incoming rays of starlight in different ways, yielding a blurry image. If the mirror's surface could be continually adjusted hundreds of times each second in such a way as to counteract the turbulent effects of the atmosphere, seeing effects could be canceled and the image sharpness improved by as much as ten to fifty times.

The idea, called "adaptive optics," was originally proposed by astronomer Horace W. Babcock in 1953. At the time, of course, such a feat was technologically impossible. Today, however, in a world of high-tech electronics and computer controls, adaptive mirrors are proving quite an effective tool.

The 3.6-meter New Technology Telescope (NTT) of the European Southern Observatory (ESO) uses a mirror attached to a network of fifty-two motorized actuators that can make slow corrections in the mirror's shape to compensate for flexure, focus, and changes in temperature. Since beginning operation in 1989, the NTT has produced infrared images as sharp as 0.18 arc second across. Since such a system can be constructed for only a few hundred thousand dollars, it becomes a bargain when used to improve the performance of existing multimillion-dollar telescopes.

While astronomers extol the virtues of adaptive optics, they are not unaware of its problems. The intricate optical system necessary to perform the mirror adjustments forces a loss of some of the precious light captured by the telescope, and since large mirrors observe through a wider column of turbulent air than smaller mirrors, they require more complicated corrections to unscramble the starlight from each point on the mirror's surface. To reduce these problems, an alternative to installing complex instrumentation at the telescope's huge primary mirror (where light is first captured from the stars) is to implement the adaptive optics at its smaller secondary mirror (which bends the light back toward a focus).

Several groups are now trying to increase the sensitivities of their adaptive optics systems. Using techniques developed by the U.S. military for the Strategic Defense Initiative, these scientists are using powerful lasers to project artificial stars onto the sky near their targets as a sufficiently bright reference source. When the deformable mirror corrects the light of the artificial "star," it also corrects the image of the nearby astronomical target. A detector then collects the image and separates the real object from the laser beam.

Perhaps most important to planet seekers, scientists are now improving the technique for use with infrared wavelengths. Not only is infrared a spectral region where atmospheric distortion is less pronounced, it is also the place where extrasolar planets are more likely to appear. Since image sharpness should improve by a factor of ten with this technique, ground-based telescopes should be able to observe objects a hundred times fainter than now possible. Through these new technologies, astronomers may soon be able to perform a variety of high-resolution studies of planet-forming regions around young or newborn stars.

As powerful as this technique may be, even more visual acuity is possible, with resolutions as fine as a few thousandths of an arc second. To accomplish such a mind-boggling task, astronomers are borrowing a technique commonly used by radio astronomers: interferometry. Interferometry uses two or more widely spaced telescopes looking at a single object whose light waves are all carefully aligned. The technique then examines the differences in the times that light waves from the same source reach the two different instruments, and simulates the resolving power of a single mirror as large as the separation between the linked instruments.

Now while radio astronomers have used this technique for decades, only recently have optical astronomers begun their experiments. That is because with radio emissions, whose wavelengths range mostly between a millimeter and many meters in length, the precision of the telescopes is not that critical. For optical astronomy, however, where wavelengths are only a fraction of a micron in length, it is another story altogether. Here, the positions of the various telescopes and the shape of the incoming wave fronts must remain highly stable. Absolute precision is required. Since large telescopes look through wide, variable columns of the atmosphere, it becomes even more difficult to keep light hitting one part of the mirror in phase with that hitting another part.

While many challenges remain for those exploring optical interferometry, the rewards will be tremendous. Calculations show that an array of moderately sized optical telescopes 200 meters apart can work in concert to produce resolutions as small as 0.002 arc second with infrared radiation, and as tiny as 0.0005 with red light.

Such clarity of vision was unheard of even a few years ago. It may, for the first time, enable astronomers to study the planet-forming disks around hundreds of young solar-type stars and even examine their innermost regions, where Earth-like planets may exist.

KECK II: THE SEQUEL

As high-powered and futuristic as all this may seem, such optical arrays are not all that far away. In April of 1991, the W. M. Keck Foundation announced it would grant up to $74.6 million toward the construction of a second, identical instrument a short distance away from the currently operating Keck telescope. Astronomers know it as Keck II.

Sitting on a ridge 85 meters away from Keck I, Keck II experienced "first light" in 1995. In that year, it began operation as a separate 10-meter telescope, gathering as much light as Keck I, and four times more than the Hale reflector on Palomar Mountain. In the following year, Keck II will team with Keck I to create the largest and most powerful optical interferometer in history. Together, these two giants will experience the light-gathering power of a single 14.1-meter-diameter mirror, and the resolving power of an 85-meter telescope. This is equivalent to discerning a car's two headlights separately from a distance of more than 25,000 kilometers away—or one-tenth of the way to the moon.

So promising is this telescope combination that NASA plans to contribute $35.5 million—one-sixth of the total cost of the telescope pair—toward the construction of Keck II. In return, NASA astronomers would receive one-sixth of the telescope's observing time to search for planets in the glare of nearby stars.

However, Keck I and II are not the only optical interferometers coming on line during the 1990s. Astronomers at the European Southern Observatory are developing an even more ambitious program. Their plan is to construct on the 2,664-meter-high peak of Cerro Paranal, Chile, a group of eight 1-meter telescopes, and four 8.2-meter behemoths that would be electronically linked to form a 190-meter-wide interferometric array. By first light in 1997, the VLT (Very Large Telescope) would likely produce resolutions of 0.002 arc second, equivalent to that produced by a single telescope 190 meters across.

Ultimately, however, the planetary quest must turn to space, high above the turbulent and obscuring atmosphere of Earth, for only there can planet hunters ever hope to achieve a totally clear and unobstructed view.

THE HUBBLE SPACE TELESCOPE

The Hubble Space Telescope (HST) was launched eight years late, but not since Galileo first turned his "optik tube" skyward in 1610 did astronomers have such high hopes for a telescope. Hubble's 2.4-meter-diameter mirror was heralded as the most perfect ever made, with surface variations less than 3×10^{-5} millimeters high—so perfect, in fact, that if the mirror were scaled up to the size of the Gulf of Mexico, its "waves" would be only 5 millimeters high. An added bonus was the telescope's high-tech instrumentation.

The Wide Field/Planetary Camera (WF/PC, pronounced "wifpik") is so remarkable that it can record in just one minute objects 4,000 times fainter than those visible to the naked eye. The Faint Object Camera (FOC) has a narrower field of view, but can discern the head or tail of a nickel from a distance of nearly 10 kilometers. Two spectrographs spread out starlight into their component colors to help scientists learn such physical properties as chemical composition, abundances, temperature, radial and rotational velocity, and magnetic field strengths of their target stars. Finally, the Fine Guidance Sensors used to aim the telescope are so accurate that, if located in New York City, they could find and lock onto a single star in the American flag as far away as Los Angeles. This highly accurate positioning system can help astronomers perform precision astrometry on stars ten times farther away than is now possible.

From its perch 600 kilometers above the Earth's turbulent atmosphere, this sophisticated instrument was designed to see objects fifty times fainter than is possible with even the largest and most powerful telescopes on Earth, and to produce an image ten times sharper than the best Earth-bound telescopes can. While the Hubble telescope was designed to peer into the deepest, darkest regions of the universe to solve fundamental cosmological mysteries, it was also capable of studying nearby objects with unprecedented clarity. In fact, it was this remarkable visual acuity, coupled with its location in space, that many astronomers hoped would enable the first successful search for planets in orbit around nearby stars.

Unfortunately, the telescope's first image showed that only 15 percent of the light captured by its mirror was focused into a sharp image. The rest was spread into a fuzzy halo surrounding the image, an affliction known as spherical aberration. For all the precision in the mirror's surface, the manufacturer had made the mirror too flat—not by much—by only about one-fiftieth the width of a human hair.

The stability and aiming of the telescope were also in danger because its giant solar panels expanded and contracted slightly each time it crossed the day-night terminator, producing a "jitter" that knocked the telescope off target. Three of its six gyroscopes failed, leaving the telescope without even one backup, and two magnetometers, which measure the telescope's orientation within Earth's magnetic field, began experiencing intermittent problems. One of the computer's six memory units failed completely and another partially, and a faulty power supply occasionally forced the use of only one of the two independent detector systems of the Goddard High Resolution Spectrograph (GHRS).

For a telescope with such promise as Hubble, these problems were serious enough to prevent astronomers from carrying out the precision work that they had planned. Soon, Hubble became the butt of jokes, cartoons, and scathing editorials and since the telescope cost nearly $2 billion, taxpayers were understandably upset. Yet, even with its problems, Hubble radioed back to Earth data at a rate of up to a million bits per second—fast enough to transmit the contents of a thirty-volume encyclopedia in only forty-two minutes.

One of its most astounding discoveries came in December of 1992, when Hubble found that up to 40 percent of the newborn stars in the Orion nebula, a huge gaseous and dusty star-forming region in the constellation Orion, are surrounded by dense, flattened protoplanetary disks. Some of these were so thick that they appear in the image only in silhouette. Others produce their own light, as ultraviolet radiation from nearby stars causes their edges to glow. Until the image was taken, only four such protoplanetary disks had ever been confirmed, and those appeared to be relatively old—perhaps 100 million years old or so. The disks of Orion, however, seemed to be a few million years old at most, and they appeared to contain at least 15 Jupiters' worth of planet-forming material that may still be contracting from the nebula itself.

Although astronomers learned to enhance the blurry images,

allowing them to make such important astronomical discoveries, they were far from satisfied. However, HST was designed to be serviced in orbit—to be visited every three years or so by astronauts who would replace failed components and upgrade instruments with newer, state-of-the-art instruments—so scientists had a chance to improve the telescope.

During the shuttle mission that began on December 2, 1993, two pairs of astronauts spent five six-hour days in the orbiter's payload bay to perform the necessary work. Together they replaced the telescope's High Speed Photometer with a Corrective Optics Space Telescope Axial Replacement (COSTAR), which holds correcting mirrors in front of the remaining scientific instruments; replaced the telescope's WF/PC with a more state-of-the-art version (WF/PC II), replaced the faulty gyroscopes, magnetometers, and solar arrays; and installed a state-of-the-art computer coprocessor to extend the computer's memory and increase the speed of some of its operations.

Though the "orbital verification" period required some three months to complete, scientists did not have to wait long to receive encouraging news about the telescope's performance. The first test images came in late December 1993 and early January 1994, and when they did, researchers cheered and toasted with champagne. The images "are about as close to perfection as engineering can achieve and the laws of physics will allow," said James H. Crocker of the Space Telescope Science Institute in Baltimore.

With its new eyesight, Hubble has improved its ability to see faint distant objects. Whereas the telescope once allowed WF/PC to concentrate only 15 percent of the incoming light into a tight focus, the new WF/PC II focuses 60 to 70 percent of the light. And COSTAR enables the Faint Object Camera to concentrate 85 percent of incoming light into the same tight focus. As a result of these and other changes, the Hubble telescope now has ten times the typical resolution of the world's largest telescope on Mauna Kea, the 10-meter Keck telescope.

Whether Hubble will be able to successfully search for extrasolar planets now that these improvements have been made is subject to much debate. In principle, the telescope can search for planets in two distinct ways: directly and indirectly. The *indirect* approach looks at the wobbling motion that a star might display as a result of the gravitational tugging of an unseen planetary companion—either side to side (by astrometry) or toward and away (by spectroscopy). However, Hubble's capability in these areas is not better than those of present ground-based telescopes.

One who hopes to measure stars' positions and detect any wobbling motion is James Westphal, a planetary scientist at the California Institute of Technology and principal investigator on Hubble's Wide Field/Planetary Camera. With WF/PC II, Westphal's team hopes to take advantage of the telescope's ability to see sharper star images by examining the positions of all stars within 10 light-years of Earth in search of wobbling motions. While such observations from space may reveal tinier wobbles than could ever be seen from beneath the wavering atmosphere of Earth, such a project will undoubtedly take an enormous amount of time.

Another way scientists hope Hubble might reveal extrasolar planets is by *direct* imaging. The trick is to block the bright light of the parent star and record the region surrounding it. Since star images are much sharper and tinier as seen from Hubble, astronomers hope not only to examine an area much closer to a star, but also to see fainter objects than now possible from Earth.

Another possibility for direct imaging lies at infrared wavelengths, where the relative brightness between star and planet would, perhaps, be reduced enough to make planets visible. That is why a team of astronomers at the University of Arizona is building a near-infrared camera (NICMOS) to be installed on Hubble in 1997. The infrared cameras in this instrument will use state-of-the-art infrared arrays consisting of 65,536 detectors cooled by solid nitrogen to hundreds of degrees below zero in order to reduce the chances that it will be blinded by its own heat.

Before astronomers can gain true insights into the nature of protoplanetary disks, or know how common they are and how likely it is that planets have already begun to form within them, other, more powerful and dedicated infrared telescopes are needed. One of the greatest is now being designed at NASA's Jet Propulsion Laboratory for launch early next decade. It is known as SIRTF, the Space Infrared Telescope Facility.

IRAS: THE NEXT GENERATION

Beginning early next century, the Space Infrared Telescope Facility (SIRTF) will build on the success of IRAS (the Infrared Astronomy Satellite), which scanned the heavens through its 0.6-meter eye in 1983 and showed for the first time disks of dusty material surrounding nearby stars.

SIRTF will use a superbly instrumented and supercooled telescope to view the infrared universe from its orbit around the sun. With a larger primary mirror than IRAS (0.85 meter in diameter), its much more powerful electronic detectors, and its more sophisticated pointing system, SIRTF will be able to detect infrared sources thousands of times fainter and create images hundreds of times sharper than did IRAS. Furthermore, with a cooling tank holding 4,000 liters of liquid helium, SIRTF should survive at least five years, six times longer than IRAS.

Because of the new technology onboard, coupled with its unique sun-centered orbit, SIRTF will accomplish more than IRAS. "It's hard to put it into words," says Dr. George Rieke of the University of Arizona, "but it's fantastically better. I once worked out an amazing fact, that with just three days of observing on SIRTF, I'll be able to make observations that, when I started in infrared astronomy around 1970, would have taken the life of the universe to complete. There are only a few moments in any area of science where it's within your grasp technically to do something that is a real breakthrough. And SIRTF is one of those moments."

By applying SIRTF's high resolution capability to the study

of circumstellar material around other stars, astronomers hope to probe the disks' dimensions, structure, and chemical composition, and to peer into their centers to learn if the dusty material extends inward toward each star, or if gaps exist where planets may have already begun to coalesce. Even a planet barely more massive than Jupiter around a nearby star should fall well within SIRTF's range. "And once we've found something like that," says Rieke, "then the spectrograph [can be used to study its atmosphere]. Presumably it would have an atmosphere a lot like Jupiter's, with zillions of infrared features of hydrocarbons, and that will be one of the main ways I think we'll confirm that we really have something resembling a planet of our solar system."

THE ASTROMETRIC IMAGING TELESCOPE

Of all the telescopes now being used or planned for extrasolar planetary searches, only the Astrometric Imaging Telescope (AIT) is totally dedicated to that purpose. During its multiyear survey of the positions and motions of stars around the sky, the 1.5- or 2-meter space-borne AIT may find planets as small as Uranus and Neptune around hundreds of stars.

The AIT began not as a single idea, but as a combination of two unique and separate concepts designed to detect extrasolar planets in different ways. The first concept emphasized astrometric detection and, not surprisingly, came from George Gatewood's observations with the Multichannel Astrometric Photometer (MAP) now being used at the University of Pittsburgh's Allegheny Observatory. Scientists expect this instrument to be able to detect Uranus- and Neptune-sized planets around more than 100 different stars. Unfortunately, this work will require at least a decade of measurements to cover a large fraction of one of these planets' orbits.

The second concept emphasized direct imaging with a coronagraphic camera like that used to record the circumstellar disk around Beta Pictoris. After JPL astronomer Richard Terrile's interest in extrasolar planets was piqued by his work on Beta Pic, his subsequent studies showed that to block out the light from a parent star in order to reveal the faint nearby image of an orbiting planet, much-improved coronagraphs were necessary. He found that by replacing the totally opaque disk used to block the starlight with a transparent one with a soft edge, the efficiency of the coronagraph could be boosted by a factor of 10 or even 100. With this instrument, scientists hope to record directly Jupiter-sized bodies around as many as fifty different stars, possibly in only a matter of hours.

Near the end of the 1980s, these two research groups merged their projects and proposed a single space-borne Astrometric Imaging Telescope (AIT) with two onboard instruments. The heart of the AIT is its supersmooth optics, about fifteen times smoother than those of the Hubble telescope. Such precision is required to reduce light scattered from the mirrors themselves, light that can overwhelm that of a faint, nearby planet. To overcome this obstacle, JPL researchers used remarkably smooth mirror technology from the semiconductor industry and managed to reduce the scattered light by a factor of 100.

For now, scientists wait patiently for the opportunity to fly the telescope. "We're ready to go," says Terrile. "It's not the technology that's keeping us back. It's [just a matter of] when NASA would be ready to engage in something like this. We're hopeful that, in the very near future, we could put up a system which would directly image, and give us an entirely new perspective on, planets in orbit around distant stars."

SPACE SUPERSCOPE?

To date, not one extrasolar planet has ever been found conclusively with current telescopes. "Very clearly we'd do better with a larger mirror," says Terrile. "I mean, every little meter helps, as we say in the business. We'd love to see larger telescopes." Astronomers continue to look far beyond the first planetary discovery itself. "First, we see planetary detection as not really the main goal," says Terrile. "We believe that they're out there. It's almost inevitable when you think about how many stars there are in our galaxy. We know from looking at the planets within our own solar system and from [the stars of the] solar neighborhood that the conditions that formed our solar system are not unique. So I think that the scientific community really believes that they're out there.

"Second," says Terrile, "we're not interested only in detection, but in the characterization of these planets. It's this second step that's going to require larger and more sophisticated instruments to break up a planet's light into a spectrum to learn what planetary atmospheres are made of, to discover oceans, to discover continental masses."

Some even believe that, with such large orbiting telescopes, one could even discover the spectral signatures of life itself. "If you looked at the Earth from the Alpha Centauri [star system] with a capable enough instrument," explains Terrile, "you would discover very easily that the Earth has a tremendous abundance of free oxygen in its atmosphere. Since oxygen is so reactive, it would [naturally] combine with almost anything on the surface. So something must be maintaining that oxygen. You'd also find a detectable signal of methane, which also has a very short lifetime in an atmosphere. So something is actively producing methane as well. We know, of course, because we live here, that the nonequilibrium chemistry is due to life. All you need [to discover this] are a few photons of light, a capable enough system, and some brain power to piece it all together."

A few astronomers have even begun to look many decades into the future, when the detection of extrasolar planets becomes routine, and the field of "comparative planetology" is booming. One of those visionaries is University of Arizona astronomer Roger Angel. When not working on his successful mirror spin-casting operation, Roger Angel dreams of the day when a powerful space telescope—a 16-meter behemoth that would dwarf all others that have come before it—is built, one that could detect planets the size and temperature of Earth at vast distances.

Angel got the idea after meeting with his colleagues to discuss the future of NASA over the next quarter century. One of the exciting ideas bandied about was the possible use of an optical interferometer that would search for extrasolar planets from the lunar surface. After thinking it out, Angel realized that such a search might be far more productive if performed with infrared radiation than with visible light. "I thought to myself," he recalls, "maybe this is what an eight-meter telescope in space could do. Unfortunately, the numbers [indicated] that eight meters is just too small. We had to go to sixteen, which is kind of outrageous, as the successor to the Hubble telescope. Nevertheless, it's what the science says we've got to have to solve this incredible problem."

Angel's superscope would feature four 8-meter mirrors assembled in a unique diamond configuration, all cooled to a temperature of 80 degrees above absolute zero. Together these mirrors would gather as much light as a single 16-meter telescope, but with the four mirrors acting as an infrared interferometer. Each would need to be polished to a smoothness equivalent to that of the Hubble telescope to prevent a star's glare from obliterating the faint light of a nearby planet or from causing effects that could masquerade as one. To help overcome this problem, Angel proposes using a system of apodized—or partially masked—mirrors that would darken the region around a star and help a planet's light shine through unobstructed.

Perhaps more amazing than the telescope itself are the sights that it would see. For example, planets the size of Jupiter could never escape its powerful eye. "Those would be duck soup," says Angel. "This thing will be able to map out entire solar systems in detail. It'll be able to find the major planets of other systems and do spectroscopy of their atmospheres. A [decent] spectrum of an Earth-like planet as far away as thirty-three light-years could be obtained in only a week or two." And in that spectrum may be features produced by the metabolic activity of life itself: oxygen, ozone, and methane.

"I think, for the first time, this telescope would be able to look at dozens of really good candidate stars like the sun which could very likely have planets like the Earth around them. So, one would hope that, unless there's something really weird about our solar system, we'd actually see planets of the right size, temperature, and atmosphere [for life]. To me, that would be absolutely fascinating."

When such a space superscope might even begin searching the skies is anyone's guess. Since it's a step or two in complexity beyond the Hubble telescope or others of the past, which cost around a billion dollars and required about two decades to design, build, and launch, such an instrument may not be built for several generations. "But, in a sense," says Angel, "it's the obvious next step for NASA. We have a fairly good understanding of our own solar system, so we can start dotting the *i*'s and crossing the *t*'s. But the attraction of looking at other systems to see if we find something much [more like] the Earth is really interesting."

A NEW ERA FOR ASTRONOMY

As humanity prepares to enter the twenty-first century, few human endeavors are proving as exciting and promising as the search for planets and planetary systems around distant stars. Many astronomers fully expect that the new generation of telescopes and instrumentation will accomplish this feat, and enable the characterization of these planets individually. And when this task begins, the next and most logical question will be: Are there beings out there wondering whether they, too, are alone?

8

W O R L D S   A L I V E ?

Despite the best efforts of astronomers to date, no planets have ever been found in orbit around distant stars. Yet every reason exists to believe that such worlds are plentiful—that millions of stars throughout the Milky Way galaxy are orbited by planets of all sizes and varieties. Most astronomers believe it is only a matter of time until they develop the technology and skill to isolate these bodies from the glare of their parent stars. In the meantime, however, some visionaries are peering beyond these yet-to-be-made discoveries, and are asking the next, most logical questions: If these worlds exist in the numbers astronomers believe, is it possible that some are home to life?

Just as the search for other planets and planetary systems depends heavily upon scientists' understanding of their chemical and physical origins, so, too, does the search for extraterrestrial life. So before one can ever hope to learn of its existence, let alone study it, the origin of life must first be understood. Today, the only world *known* to contain life is the Earth.

No one knows with certainty how life began on Earth. Some scientists believe it began rather quickly, perhaps within only 500 million years of the planet's birth 4.6 billion years ago. Some suspect that living cells are an inevitable product of organic chemistry that should occur naturally on *any* world where such chemistry exists. Others believe that life descended from one simple cell that, coincidentally, came into being here on Earth, and that the chances of an identical combination of chemical and physical conditions existing on a world elsewhere in the universe are slim at best.

Scientists are fairly certain that, during the early history of the Earth's existence, volcanoes were quite active and spewed into the sky the first atmosphere of carbon dioxide, water vapor, and ammonia. Lightning bolts ripped through the dark, noxious clouds and tore apart their molecules. When they recombined, the molecules formed simple organic compounds like glycine and adenine, the most basic building blocks of life. Eventually, scientists believe, simple inanimate chemicals came together to make up more complex structures that were able to move, digest food, grow and reproduce, forming the first living cells from which life proliferated and evolved into the countless complex structures that exist today.

In the past, the origin of life was considered possible only because the Earth is surrounded by an atmosphere containing the proper mixture of oxygen, nitrogen, and carbon dioxide, with a relatively stable temperature at which liquid water can exist. What is becoming clear, however, is that the atmospheric conditions often thought necessary for life to *begin* may, instead, be a direct product of the life itself.

Interestingly, the Earth's atmosphere is a naturally unstable and potentially explosive mixture of gases and, had it not been for living organisms, the atmosphere would be virtually devoid of the unstable elements nitrogen and oxygen. Nitrogen prefers to be "locked up" as nitrate ions in the waters of the ocean. That it exists at all is attributable, in part, to the fact that some bacteria consume the nitrates and transform them into nitrous oxide and nitrogen, maintaining the atmospheric supply of nitrogen, despite the chemical's efforts to bond with other elements. The same is true of oxygen. If left to itself, it would be removed by the oxidation of rocks, leaving the atmosphere devoid of the chemical. Molecular oxygen in the atmosphere is a by-product of the photosynthesis of microscopic plants near the ocean's surface called phytoplankton. Powered by sunlight, they turn water and carbon dioxide into free oxygen, making it possible for higher forms of life—trees, animals, and people—to flourish.

Everything that occurs on Earth, it seems, is interrelated and interdependent: if one component of life, atmosphere, water, or soil should change in some way, other changes would be forthcoming and would continue in a complex chain reaction that ultimately could affect everything. One of the most vocal supporters of this notion is the British scientist James E. Lovelock, who, in the early 1970s, developed his ideas with Boston University biologist Lynn Margulis, and wrote a book titled *The Ages of Gaia*. In his book, Lovelock explained that the ball of nonliving material that forms this planet is surrounded by an envelope of gas, water, and carbon-rich soil that supports a thriving network of life—the biosphere—and called it "Gaia," after the Greek goddess of the Earth.

Life on Earth uses this planet's atmosphere as a source of raw materials and as a repository for wastes, and prevents it from reaching an equilibrium. In this way, life controls the composition of the lower atmosphere (and hence the temperature and climate) by regulating the amount of carbon dioxide, molecular nitrogen, and molecular oxygen. For example, if the amount of sunlight falling to Earth should decrease for some reason, Gaia would respond by promoting the growth of organisms that release more carbon dioxide into the atmosphere. This would act as a blanket and maintain the overall temperature of the planet.

While this interrelationship of terrestrial components had been discussed for many years, such a holistic view of the world has become popular only since the late 1960s, when humans first left behind their home planet and journeyed to the moon. In the process, we looked back at our planet and saw it as a singular, self-contained world—an oasis of life suspended against the black and hostile void of space.

THE INGREDIENTS FOR LIFE ARE EVERYWHERE

Interestingly, the chemicals for life are found not only here on Earth, but elsewhere in space as well. Meteorites that plunge to the ground are known to be the oldest unaltered material in the solar system; they carry carbon-based compounds—alkanes, aromatics, carboxylic acids, amino acids, and others—some of which are considered crucial for the existence of life as we know it. For decades, debates have raged about whether meteorites carried these materials with them from the void of space, or whether they became "contaminated" only after entering the Earth's atmosphere and striking the planet's surface. In addition, recent research has shown that meteorites are rich in deuterium, a form of hydrogen twice as heavy as the more common form and far more common in interstellar space than here on Earth. Evidence today suggests that these chemicals existed in the meteorites long before they began their final plunge to Earth.

Farther from home, the chemical constituency of many interstellar clouds has been determined over the past few decades. Since the discovery of methylidyne (CH) in space in 1937, four simple molecules were found in space during the next quarter century. Three were detected by their emission of visible radiation and one by its radio waves. Then, in the late 1960s, astronomers used radio and other telescopes to step up their search for even more complex chemical species by seeking the telltale radiations emitted by the vibrations of specific molecules. To date, astronomers have found evidence for some six dozen kinds of molecules in space. That these exist in such numbers should not be surprising since, within these thick interstellar clouds, the delicate bonds between atoms are protected from the devastating effects of ultraviolet radiation emanating from nearby stars.

Many of the chemicals found in interstellar space are rather simple. Some, like hydrogen, are built from the most common material in the universe, and are simply two hydrogen atoms bound together into a molecule. Others are much more complex. Molecules of such common substances as alcohol, carbon monoxide, ammonia, and water have been found as well. Some, like cyanodecapentyne, are composed of as many as thirteen atoms linked together.

Interestingly, most of these interstellar molecules are carbon based—they are the same "organic" materials that form the building blocks out of which all life on Earth is made. The predominance of carbon, hydrogen, nitrogen, and oxygen in the molecules is even more fascinating, since these four atoms are known to be the critical ingredients of building blocks such as protein and DNA. Their prevalence and ability to form and exist virtually anywhere suggests that if life does exist beyond Earth, it may feature a chemistry similar to that right here at home.

Yet, until recently, only individual molecules had been found in meteorites. They had never been found linked into chains known here as polymers, though their presence had been strongly suspected. In 1986, though, a multinationally sponsored robot spacecraft named *Giotto* encountered the gaseous coma, or head, of Halley's comet and saw the first "chain" of molecules ever detected in space. The polymer turned out to be a form of formaldehyde, known to chemists as polyoxymethylene, or POM, and to the rest of us as embalming fluid. This strengthened the view that comets may be repositories of some of the most primitive materials in the solar system—veritable frozen time capsules left over from the primordial nebula out of which the sun, its planetary family, and life itself were formed. The discovery suggested that the chemistry of life is not only something that exists here on Earth, but might be found anywhere at any time, an exciting prospect indeed.

CHECKING OUT THE NEIGHBORS

Finding chemicals on rocks and within the dusty clouds of interstellar space is one thing, but detecting evidence that these molecules might have combined and evolved into recognizable life-forms on other worlds is something entirely different. While humans have gazed into the heavens and wondered about our uniqueness since the beginning of time, it has been only within the past few decades that scientists have been armed with solid leads and the technology with which to follow them up. Certainly, the easiest place to conduct a search for direct evidence is on the worlds closest to home—the planets and satellites of our own solar system.

In the 1960s, astronauts first ventured to the moon and analyzed its soil for microorganisms, even though scientists knew that conditions there were not conducive to life—it contains virtually no atmosphere or water, and its surface is continually bombarded by intense ultraviolet radiation from the sun and cosmic rays from beyond. Still, when the astronauts returned home, officials placed them in quarantine for several days—just to make sure they hadn't brought back some strange lunar virus or microorganism. As it turned out, few places could be drier or more lifeless than the moon.

There were other worlds, however, where the probability of finding living organisms seemed higher. The world that, for nearly a century, had captured the imagination most was within reach: Mars. Photographs of the Red Planet taken by the *Mariner* spacecraft in the 1960s showed conclusively no evidence of large life-forms of any kind—and certainly not the intelligent canal builders imagined by Percival Lowell. No one could imagine what kind of macro-organisms could survive with virtually no water in the planet's thin, cold, carbon dioxide atmosphere. But tiny microbes, algae or bacteria, might be a different story. Certainly places on Earth exist that appear at first glance to be quite barren—Antarctica and the deserts of Africa—but which are

teeming with life on a microscopic scale. If a diversity of micro-
bial life can survive the harsh heat, cold, and dryness of these
regions, could it also exist on Mars?

To find out, two robot spacecraft were launched toward the
Red Planet and set down on Mars in July of 1976. The probes
were the first from Earth to make a soft, controlled landing on
this alien world. *Viking 1* landed on one side of the planet, in
the region known as Chryse Planitia; a few days later, *Viking 2*
set down on the opposite side of the planet. Their task was to
analyze the weather, geology, and chemistry of the landing sites
in a way that had never been done before. Perhaps even more
intriguing, however, the *Vikings* were to conduct a direct search
for martian life.

Day after day their cameras snapped panoramic photographs
of the area surrounding the landing sites, searching for signs of
movement. Their automated shovels dug into the martian soil
and delivered samples to the spacecraft interior to be tested for
the presence of microorganisms. The idea was that if martian life
were carbon based and behaved similarly to Earth life, it should
alter its environment enough to be detected by analyzing either
the atmospheric gases or the soil of Mars. To assure that the
spacecraft would not contaminate the martian environment with
organisms brought from Earth, both were baked in an oven at
temperatures hotter than boiling water for three days to sterilize
the craft before they were sealed in capsules to be launched into
space.

One of the tests Viking performed was the gas exchange
(GEX), known affectionately to researchers as the "chicken
soup" experiment. The robots added water and organic and in-
organic nutrients to the soil with the idea that if martian creatures
consumed the mix, they would expel gases, enabling Viking to
measure their presence by their biological waste products above
the soil sample. Another test was the labeled release (LR) experiment, designed to examine the soil more directly for biological activity. Once again, nutrients were dripped onto the soil,
but not just ordinary nutrients; these had had their carbon atoms

replaced with radioactive carbon atoms. The concept was that animal cells should ingest these isotopes and exhale radioactive carbon dioxide or methane, both of which could be detected by the spacecraft. A positive measurement would suggest that organisms had gobbled up the nutrients and had released gases into the atmosphere.

The third procedure was called the pyrolytic release (PR) experiment, and was designed to look for photosynthesis. Martian soil samples were incubated for five days in an environment similar to that on the planet—complete with artificial light designed to mimic that of the sun. The only difference was that the atmospheric carbon dioxide and carbon monoxide were tagged with radioactive carbon; if microscopic organisms incorporated the carbon atoms by photosynthesis, they would become slightly radioactive. After the five days, the atmosphere would be removed, and the soil samples heated to 638 degrees Celsius to incinerate the martian organisms and drive off the radioactive carbon atoms for detection by a counting device.

Before the life experiments could begin, however, scientists wanted to test the martian soil and learn its composition. The first of the soil tests were performed with a highly sophisticated gas chromatograph–mass spectrometer (or GCMS) and the results were radioed to waiting scientists on Earth. In each of two samples tested at each site, *Viking* found no traces of organic compounds. To make sure that the soil hadn't been affected by the sun's deadly ultraviolet radiation getting through the planet's thin atmosphere, *Viking* even dug beneath a rock for a sample. Again, the results were negative. Not one organic compound had been found. This was not an encouraging result for potential martian biologists, for without organic compounds, life as we know it could not exist there.

Now one might argue that from tests carried out at two extremely remote sites on the planet, one should not draw a broad conclusion for the entire planet. While this might be true on any other world, Mars is known to experience tremendous wind storms that pick up and carry dust from one part of the planet to another—at times becoming so large and violent that they obliterate from terrestrial view the entire planet's surface. No part of the planet is immune from this treatment either, and this means that soil around the globe must be intermixed with that from every other part. In other words, soil tests in Chryse Planitia could be assumed to be fairly representative of those from any other site on Mars. From this reasoning, and the results of the GCMS experiments, scientists were forced to conclude that no organic compounds existed on Mars, and that life as we know it could not exist on this alien world. That's why they were so shocked when all three of the life experiments returned positive results! Something strange was definitely taking place on Mars.

Viking 1 began the first of its life-seeking tests eight days after landing. Two days later, scientists examined the GEX results and found fifteen times more oxygen in the chamber than they expected from the planet's atmosphere alone. Then, one day later, the LR experiment results were received. Again a positive result. How could life exist on Mars without the necessary organic building blocks anywhere to be found? What kind of life was this anyway? Was it such an efficient biological scavenger that it devoured all its wastes, foods, and their remains? Soon, the results of the (PR) experiment were received and they, too, were undeniably positive.

Scientists, being typically skeptical of experimental results that do not jibe with reason, weren't convinced that it was biological activity that caused the observed data. So, in a final attempt to solve the puzzle, they heated the soil to as high as 175 degrees Centigrade for several hours, then performed the tests again. And again the tests results came back positive. Since the average martian temperature never rises above about 30 degrees Centigrade, it seemed quite unlikely that martian organisms could possibly survive a nearly sixfold increase in temperature. It turned out, scientists now believe, that the reactions that produced such contradictory results were not biological, but purely chemical. They reasoned that because the martian soil is so dry, the addition of just a tiny amount of the liquid brought about chemical reactions that mimicked the effects of biological activity here on Earth.

Despite evidence to the contrary, there are those who believe that human or robotic explorers may one day find martian life—perhaps near the planet's northern polar ice cap, where pools of liquid water may exist during martian summers. At the least, they are hoping that evidence of life in Mars's distant past will be found—fossils in the deep canyon walls carved by raging rivers of water hundreds of millions of years ago when atmospheric conditions and temperatures were presumably more conducive to life. Perhaps it is here that future explorers may uncover fossils of long-extinct martian organisms. Until that day, however, scientists must base their conclusions on the evidence in hand: that Mars is, and always has been, devoid of life as we know it.

Of all the worlds in the Solar System, it has always been Mars that seemed the likeliest candidate for alien life, but upon closer inspection, other worlds present quite an intriguing array of possibilities as well. One is the giant planet Jupiter. Jupiter's atmosphere is known to professional and amateur astronomers alike as a colorful place with swirling storms and belts of clouds visible to even the smallest backyard telescopes. Interestingly, much of the color of its clouds comes from organic compounds—the basis for life as we know it. While Jupiter has no surface on which life could form and exist, beneath its visible face lies a world of increasing temperature. Somewhere between its frozen cloudtops and its searing core must lie a region where temperatures are mild enough that liquid water could exist. Combine liquid water, organic chemistry, and ultraviolet radiation from tremendous lightning storms on the planet, and it does not seem entirely impossible that rudimentary forms of life may have formed there. Some scientists have even speculated—partially tongue-in-cheek—that a race of huge bloated "fish" may float among the Jovian clouds, gobbling up organic materials in the enormous atmosphere.

Even on Titan, the largest moon of the ringed planet Saturn, some researchers believe that life may have gotten started. Titan's atmosphere had long appeared similar to that of the Earth some 4 billion years ago, back when the first single-celled terrestrial creatures were beginning to form. Is it possible that somewhere on its surface are pools of organic "goo" in which the building blocks of life are just now beginning to coalesce into life? While much remains unknown about this alien world, the robot space-craft *Voyager 1* did show that the nitrogen atmosphere of Titan is unable to retain heat, and that the temperature there hovers at nearly −184 degrees Celsius. It seems now that if life does exist on Titan, it is exceedingly hardy.

From an extensive survey of the dozens of worlds that make up the sun's family, most scientists have concluded that the only life anywhere—certainly the only *intelligent* life—exists right here on planet Earth. So many are turning their attention to finding worlds among the stars on which life may have arisen.

HOW PREVALENT ARE THEY?

Scientists estimate that beyond the solar system, there could exist between 3 million and 15 million potential life-supporting plan-ets within the Milky Way galaxy alone, with possibly many mil-lions of technological civilizations inhabiting them. The numbers, of course, are mere guesses: nobody has yet to find more than one (Earth) that fits the bill. That any could exist at all may depend on a remarkably precise balance among several measurable properties of the universe.

For example, if the force of gravity were just a bit stronger, the gravitational tug-of-war within a star would be different. Its internal pressures would be greater and its temperatures higher. Most stars in such a "heavyweight" universe might become hot blue giants that would exhaust their fuel far too rapidly for life to thrive on nearby planets. If, on the other hand, the gravita-tional constant were just a bit smaller than it is, then most stars might become red dwarfs, and would be far too cool to support life on nearby planets.

The expansion rate of the universe is also of prime importance in determining the existence of other worlds and other life. If the universe were expanding more rapidly than it is (say, by only one part in 10^{60}), galaxies themselves might never have formed. If the expansion were any slower (perhaps by the same amount), the combined gravitational attraction of all the galaxies might have caused the universe to collapse back upon itself long ago. As it turns out, the universe is expanding at just the right rate to have enabled galaxies and stars to form, chemical elements to be forged inside of stars, and planets and life to originate—at least on one planet.

With such remarkable balance in the physical laws that govern the cosmos, the universe seems mathematically and physically "destined" to produce worlds and life. Is it possible that this is just one of many universes whose physical and chemical properties are all quite different? Does our Earth and its life exist because it was *this* universe whose properties just *happened* to be balanced in such a way as to make life possible? Or do we exist at some special and unique time and place that is, perhaps, the product of divine intervention?

These are issues that will undoubtedly be debated by scientists and theologians for decades to come but one thing is certain. Since this universe *does* exist, and since life thrives nicely on at least one world within, the universe is obviously *capable* of producing worlds and life. And scientists believe that both are out there in tremendous numbers.

Before anyone can turn such wild speculation into certainty, however, a number of important quantities must be defined. For example, of the tremendous number of stars in the Milky Way galaxy alone, how many are actually endowed with planetary systems? How many of these contain planets that are ecologically suited for life as we know it? How many of *these* suitable worlds have given rise to life—not just any life—but an intelligent life which has developed the desire and technology to communicate across the cosmos?

In 1961, astronomer Frank Drake incorporated these questions into a single equation that today bears his name—the Drake equation. It came about while Drake was trying to organize the first scientific meeting on the subject of extraterrestrial life. "I needed a way to decide what the subject of each section would be," recalls Drake. "And I recognized that you can describe the whole business by that one equation." Drake's equation determines the number of advanced technological civilizations that may exist in the galaxy (N) by considering all the physical, biological, and sociological factors necessary for its existence. It reads like this:

$$N = N^* f_p n_e f_l f_i f_c f_L$$

The first two terms on the right side of the equation are physical quantities, and are reasonably well known. N^* represents the number of stars in the Milky Way galaxy, and f_p represents the fraction of these stars that have planetary systems. The next three terms give biological information, and are not yet quantifiable: n_e, the number of planets in a given system that are ecologically suitable for life; f_l, the fraction of otherwise suitable planets on which life actually arises; and f_i, the fraction of inhabited planets on which intelligent life evolves. Finally come two terms that are sociological in nature: f_c, the fraction of planets inhabited by intelligent beings who have developed technology capable of communicating; and f_L, the fraction of a planetary lifetime graced by a technological civilization.

While only one of the terms in this formula is known with any degree of certainty—the number of stars within the galaxy—one can estimate numbers based on scientific guesses to calculate the possible number of worlds that may have given rise to life as we know it, and how many civilizations might exist with whom we might one day establish contact.

For example, astronomers know with reasonable certainty the number of stars in the Milky Way (N*): around 400 billion. Recent evidence suggests that perhaps half of these stars may have planetary systems around them (f_p = 0.5). If so, then some 200 billion stars in the Milky Way galaxy alone may be orbited by planets. However, only a certain number of these planetary systems may contain ecological conditions suitable for life as we know it.

Every star has a "zone of habitability"—a region in which planets at a certain range would receive just the right amount of heat to support life *as we know it*. If a planet exists within this region, life might begin and evolve, but only if its temperature lies between 0 and 100 degrees Celsius so that liquid water can exist. If the Earth were only a few percent closer to the sun, it would not now be habitable. The extra heat would have vaporized more water and built up larger and thicker clouds, which would, in turn, hold in more heat, which would continue vaporizing water. It was just this runaway "greenhouse" effect that made Venus, a world similar in size and mass to the Earth, totally uninhabitable. If the Earth were only 1 or 2 percent farther from the sun, temperatures would be low enough so that periodic ice ages would be irreversible, and the Earth would have become a frozen desert, much like Mars is today.

From cosmic inventories, astronomers know that most stars are too small and faint to support life on orbiting planets. Their zones of habitability would be extremely small, and only those planets closest to the star could receive enough heat—but not too much—for liquid water to exist. A planet orbiting near one of these tiny red dwarf stars would need to lie less than 9.7 million kilometers from the star to receive the same amount of radiation as the Earth does from the sun. At such a small distance, the star's gravity would slow the planet's rotation so that, eventually, one of its hemispheres would always face the star, while one would face away. One side would bake and the other would freeze, making life as we know it impossible.

Other stars are so hot bright that they would shower their planets with lethal ultraviolet radiation. They might create wider zones of habitability, but they would burn their fuel so rapidly that they would die long before life had a sufficient opportunity to take hold on their worlds. These stars are quite rare, so eliminating them from consideration has only a small impact on the equation.

It seems, therefore, that those stars most likely able to support planetary systems in which there are life-bearing planets are those most like the sun. Not only do they provide zones of habitability in regions where regular planetary rotation can maintain temperatures suitable for the long-term existence of liquid water, but they survive long enough to enable life to take hold. Astronomers estimate that these make up about 1 out of every 100 stars in the galaxy (about 2 billion stars), but two-thirds of these may exist in binary systems that would disturb planetary orbits and make life there impossible. This would leave about 667 million single, sunlike stars around which such planetary systems are possible.

So how many of these might *actually* have worlds that are habitable? The best estimate comes from the only example of a planetary system ever studied: our own. While several planets and moons may have conditions where at least primitive life might exist, only Venus, Earth, and Mars lie within a zone of habitability around the sun in which liquid water can exist—a chemical we deem necessary for *life as we know it*. Since there is no reason to believe otherwise, let us suppose that other planetary systems behave like ours, and that each system has nine planets and that one-third of these lie in such habitable zones ($n_e = 0.33$). This means that in the 667 million systems that may exist, about 6 billion planets exist, and one-third of these planets lie within ecologically suitable zones.

In the Milky Way galaxy, then, as many as about 1.98 billion worlds might be home to life. But suppose life actually arises on only one out of the nine worlds ($f_l = 0.11$), as in our solar system. This would mean that 218 million worlds within the Milky Way have life of some kind. This is a tremendously exciting prospect.

The next logical question to ask, then, is how many of these worlds may be home to life that has evolved, or will eventually evolve, to some form of intelligence. Here is where the numbers really begin to break down, since every number is a wild guess. Just for the sake of argument, suppose that only 1 percent of all worlds ever see some form of life evolve to intelligence ($f_i = 0.01$). This would produce about 2.18 million worlds in the galaxy that have at least one intelligent life-form. Now, if 1 percent of those ever develop sufficient technology to listen to and beam radio signals or travel across space themselves ($f_c = 0.01$), as many as 21,800 worlds in the galaxy may have, or eventually will, give birth to at least one intelligent, technologically competent species like ourselves.

But do these civilizations exist right now? The answer to that question depends on how long a technological civilization survives. Since there is no way of knowing the answer to this question, the best guess here comes, again, from our own civilization. We humans have been able to communicate with radio for about one century, or only about two-millionths of 1 percent of the current life of our planet (f_L). If this number is typical of other civilizations—in other words, that all civilizations evolve to, but no further than our own current technological level—then it seems that one civilization must come along, or disappear, every seven and a half centuries. In other words, the number of technological civilizations like our own that may be scattered around the galaxy at this very moment might be only one—*us*!

On the other hand, the numbers used to get this result may be so far off the mark that the universe literally abounds with advanced technological civilizations. Considering the hundreds of billions of galaxies beyond the Milky Way, such an idea is not all that far-fetched. In fact, many astronomers believe that civilizations are out there in numbers far greater than anyone has ever guessed, but the numbers vary wildly from astronomer to astronomer. "They depend on who you're talking to," explains Drake. "For most of the factors we have little or, in some cases, no direct evidence of the right number. The only one we know [with any certainty] is the rate of star formation per year. All the rest are open to personal opinion at the present time, and have a wide range of values. So people invent the numbers and speculate on the basis of their concepts of the universe."

MAKING CONTACT

To practice with the concept of communicating with alien civilizations by way of such pictures, astronomers have created and sent some experimental messages. "In all of the cases," recalls Frank Drake, one of those astronomers from the University of California at Santa Cruz, "a bunch of scientists sat around and wondered what the extraterrestrials would need to know about us. We knew we didn't need to teach basic science or mathematics because [if they received the message], they know all that. What they'd want to know is what is special about us. So we tended to give a description of biochemistry or human anatomy or terrestrial biology. Of course, we don't really know what they'd like to hear from us, but that's our best guess."

The effort began with the launching of the *Pioneer 10* and *Pioneer 11* spacecraft in the early 1970s. Each spacecraft was launched to fly past and study the giant planets Jupiter and Saturn and, when their missions there were completed, to continue drifting on into the depths of space—forever. Each carried on their frames a plaque that showed a chart of the sun's location in the galaxy and other scientific information about the craft and the creatures who launched it into space. The hope was, of course, that any civilization capable of intercepting the spacecraft and message someday might also be technologically sophisticated enough to decipher and understand its message.

Long before the craft ever left the ground, one section of its "cosmic postcard" created an even greater stir right here on Earth. In their attempt to explain human structure simply and visually, scientists included on the plaque a sketch of a nude man and woman standing side by side. But not all saw the purpose of these images as noble. "There were people who thought it was an obscene thing to do," recalls Drake, "that it was smut and that we were pornographers, and that taxpayers' money shouldn't be spent on such things."

Today, the two *Pioneer* spacecraft are far beyond the solar system and continue to drift outward toward the stars. To anyone's knowledge, this modest first attempt at communication has yet to find, or morally corrupt, an extraterrestrial civilization.

A second effort came in 1977, when the robot spacecraft *Voyager 1* and *2* were also launched to the outer planets of the solar system. On each of their sides was attached a gold-plated record entitled *Sounds of Earth,* along with a stylus and symbolic instructions for operating the record. The two-hour recording contained a vast array of audio selections from our world—from biological to geological to technological to artistic, as well as human communications and electronically encoded images of our world.

Four committees assembled the various parts for the record: a music committee, a *Voices of Earth* committee, a *Sounds of Earth* committee, and a photo committee, of which Drake was the chairman. "Probably thirty-five or forty people were very actively involved for several weeks gathering material for that record. In each case, we were trying to guess what the extraterrestrials might like to hear from us."

Deciding which information and images to include on the record was a much more massive job than devising a simple plaque. "We had thousands of candidate photos [to choose from]," recalls Drake. "We [went] to books we knew that had good quality pictures in them, and we made massive raids on *National Geographic.* We all just pored over them and selected the ones we thought should go on the record. In fact, if we had had compact discs back then, it would have been just awful. It would have taken years to put together enough material to fill a CD. But the best we had then was a metal phonograph record.

It played for two hours at an information rate of about ten thousand characters per second."

As colorful and intriguing an idea as it was, it came about quite by surprise. "NASA never starts these projects until the last minute," says Drake. "They wait until a couple of months before launch and then suddenly they realize that we should put something on [the craft]. And everybody jumps through hoops to get it done." The job was particularly difficult because not only was there a tremendous amount of material to assemble and prioritize, but it all had to be converted into audio recordings with special equipment available only in Colorado Springs, Colorado. "And all this stuff had to be approved by NASA to make sure we weren't doing anything that was going to embarrass the government. So it was a pretty crash program!"

Ultimately, the two-hour recording contained 116 images and thousands of sounds representative of the Earth and its many life-forms. It featured musical selections ranging from tribal music to Beethoven to the rock 'n' roll of Chuck Berry. Its sound essay included audio selections from volcanoes to the ocean to rocket launches. Spoken messages were recorded in sixty languages, and included a message from then-President Jimmy Carter proclaiming "our wish to become a member of the galactic community."

In the late 1980s, both spacecraft headed outward beyond the planets Uranus and Neptune. *Voyager 2* left along the plane of the planetary system; *Voyager 1* at nearly a right angle to it. Yet even at their continuing speeds of nearly 2 million kilometers per day, the spacecraft would require nearly six hundred centuries to reach the nearest star, Proxima Centauri; but neither is aimed in that direction. In fact, the craft will most likely carry humanity's message for millennia before encountering anything—or *anybody*. *Voyager 2*'s next encounter may not occur for a quarter of a million years when it skirts the vicinity of the star Ross 248, one of the nearest in the Milky Way galaxy. Perhaps someday before then, the craft will be intercepted by an alien space-faring civilization who will find the record and learn about the creatures who were curious enough to send it outward in search of other worlds and other civilizations.

Not only have humans consciously launched greetings into space aboard robot spacecraft, many have broadcast radio messages to the stars as well. Ever since Guglielmo Marconi's first "wireless" transmission across the Atlantic Ocean around the turn of the twentieth century, humans have been unintentionally leaking our everyday radio, television, and radar signals into space. When a signal emanates from an antenna on Earth, it radiates outward in all directions—some of which impinge on the antenna for which it is intended. But some miss and continue outward into space at the speed of light. In other words, the Earth is surrounded by an ever-expanding shell of radio and television transmissions 80 to 90 light-years in radius.

Now, while it is true that the signals weaken as they recede from Earth by the inverse square law (double its distance, it becomes 2^2, or 4, times weaker, triple its distance and it becomes 3^2 or 9, times weaker, and so on), these waves fill a volume of space equivalent to nearly 700,000 cubic light-years. Within this space, hundreds of stars, and potentially hundreds or thousands of planets as well, may be bombarded by terrestrial radiation daily. If one of those planets is home to life whose evolutionary path has taken it on a route similar to that on Earth, its civilizations might have developed the sophisticated telescopes necessary to detect radio signals from afar. Even though the sun and its attendant family of worlds would be but an invisible speck in their sky, their radio telescope aimed in its direction (and, therefore, in the direction of Earth) might receive the signals that humans have unintentionally beamed across space for nearly a century.

A planet in orbit around the star Zeta Herculis, for example, some 31 light-years distant, might now be receiving the strains of the Beatles; others some 50 light-years distant might hear the horrors of World War II. Still others farther out might pick up the comic banter of Charley McCarthy and Edgar Bergen, or the sounds of Lindbergh crossing the Atlantic for the first time.

And what military secrets might they glean as they intercept countless radio and radar signals broadcast from nations around the Earth? If alien civilizations exist and have the technology to tune in to the Earth, they may have already learned much about us—by accident.

Not only have humans unintentionally broadcast signals toward the stars, we've done it deliberately too. In November of 1974, a group of Cornell scientists led by Dr. Carl Sagan used the powerful new 305-meter-diameter radio telescope at Arecibo, Puerto Rico, to beam a message into space. "It was done in large part because we needed something spectacular to do as part of the telescope dedication ceremonies," recalls Frank Drake, who took part in the effort. "We were trying to create a special event with that message." The signal was transmitted as a binary code—a series of ons and offs—that, when translated by a technologically sophisticated civilization, would produce for them a number of pictures that told of the beings and technology that sent the message. It was aimed in the direction of the great globular star cluster in the constellation Hercules known to scientists as M13—chosen because its hundreds of thousands of stars would increase the probability that planets might exist there where someone might be listening.

Anyone expecting a two-way conversation with beings from M13, however, is in for a surprise, for the cluster lies at a distance of roughly 21,000 light-years away. This means that the message, sent at the speed of light, will require 21,000 years to arrive at its destination. Whether the signal would even be detected is quite debatable. First, solid worlds on which intelligent life could evolve must exist within the cluster. Since the stars of M13 are extremely old and are composed of lighter, more volatile elements, the chances of solid bodies orbiting any one of them are slim. Not only must the life-form be intelligent, but it must be a technologically advanced society that has developed radio astronomy and has a large enough radio telescope to receive the message. This telescope must be aimed in just the right direction and tuned to just the right frequency before they can ever hope to hear the signal. If that's not enough, they must be listening at just the right time, for the message scientists sent was only three minutes in length. Then, if they do receive the message, they must recognize it as an intelligent signal and be able to decipher the code.

If all these conditions are met—and this is a very big "if"— the receiving civilization might decide to send a response, which, of course, would require another 21,000 years to arrive at Earth. One might wonder, then, just what the purpose of such a message is if the probability of receipt is virtually zero. The answer is that humans wish simply to broadcast our existence to the universe.

To date, our efforts at actively communicating with extraterrestrial beings have been little more than token gestures—notes in a bottle tossed to the cosmic sea. However, in the past few decades, scientists have begun to aim giant radio telescopes skyward to *listen* patiently for intelligent radio signals coming our way from among the stars of the galaxy. In 1992, NASA began a decade-long comprehensive listening program that is scanning the skies from end to end in search of alien radio messages. If such signals are out there, NASA hopes to find them.

EAVESDROPPING ON THE COSMOS

Perhaps scientists stand a greater chance of learning of others' existence by *listening* instead of transmitting. For decades, radio telescopes have been listening to a number of radio frequencies to learn about the emissions of gas clouds, galaxies, exploding stars, quasars, and pulsars. Then, in 1967, astronomers believed they had accidentally picked up a signal from an intelligent extraterrestrial civilization.

At Cambridge University's Mullard Observatory, graduate student Jocelyn Bell was studying the "twinkling" of natural celestial radio sources as their radiation was interrupted by particles blasted from the sun. Then, on November 28 of that year, the pen on her strip-chart recorder began to fluctuate wildly:

the source, it seemed, was pulsating sharply at regular intervals one second apart. Within days, Bell and her mentor Antony Hewish had determined that the source was located a few hundred light-years away from Earth. What it was, however, no one knew.

The pulses were being emitted with a precision of a millionth of a second—far greater than that of any natural radio signals ever detected—and this led the astronomers to speculate that the signals might just originate from an advanced civilization. Among their group, the astronomers called their idea the LGM (little green men) hypothesis. It was later learned, however, that the pulses had another, almost equally fantastic, origin. They were coming from a tiny, dense neutron star—the remains of a supernova explosion—that spins rapidly and funnels intense radiation out its magnetic poles, sweeping through space periodically like a lighthouse beacon.

As exciting as the LGM hypothesis was, it had not been the first false alarm ever experienced. A decade earlier, while still a graduate student at Harvard, Frank Drake encountered some "little green men" of his own. In the spring of 1957, he was studying the radio emissions emanating from the Pleiades, a star cluster visible from Earth in the constellation of Taurus. While he was observing its radio spectrum, a very narrow peak suddenly appeared. Drake's immediate reaction was that he had detected an intelligent signal from the Pleiades. To check if it really was coming from the Pleiades, Drake moved the telescope slightly. Unfortunately, the signal remained. "It turned out to be a terrestrial signal, which was really a very strange fluke," he says.

Though he was disappointed, Drake didn't give up. After all, the whole idea of extraterrestrial life was something that had fascinated him since he was a boy. By now, however, the technology to detect evidence of extraterrestrial intelligence was available, and Drake set out to do just that. "The idea developed because we were building a major new telescope at Green Bank, West Virginia. Having always been fascinated by the subject, I calculated from just how far this telescope could detect a strong signal—something like we might produce here on Earth," recalls Drake. "That showed that signals could be detected from distances of a few tens of light-years, and that we did have the ability to detect reasonable signals." So, in 1959, Drake used the 26-meter-diameter dish at Green Bank to begin the first radio search for extraterrestrial intelligence.

Drake named his project Ozma, after the princess of the mythical land of Oz in L. Frank Baum's children's stories. "I had read and enjoyed those books a lot as a child, and I remembered that Oz was a land far away, populated by strange and exotic beings, and very difficult to reach," says Drake. "That seemed like a good description of what we were trying to find." So Ozma it became.

Shortly after beginning Project Ozma, Drake experienced another "encounter." On the first day of the study, Drake had his telescope aimed in the direction of Epsilon Eridani, a sunlike star in the constellation of Eridanus. As the telescope homed in, the astronomer heard bursts of noise on a loudspeaker, and then his strip-chart recorder pen flew completely off the scale. "I felt very excited," recalls Drake. "You get a very special emotion which is hard to describe. It comes from the idea that you're seeing something very important for the first time in the history of the human race. It's a very special emotion involving awe and elation that we felt, even though at the time we were suspicious that the signal was actually a terrestrial interference signal." Within a few minutes, the signal disappeared, but Drake and his colleagues continued monitoring that frequency in case it returned. A week later it did and, this time, they learned with disappointment that their suspicions were true: the signals were coming from terrestrial radar.

So the search continued for two months more, listening for evidence that others exist out there. "We did it with very little cost so that it [couldn't be] accused of wasting resources and we actually chose the frequency at 1,420 megahertz so the equipment would also be useful for conventional astronomy programs.

Unfortunately, we never found a good candidate in Project Ozma."

Then, in 1977, astronomers at the Ohio State University received dramatic radio signals that appeared out of nowhere. It was dubbed the "Wow" signal, after the comment by one of the researchers. The signals seemed to be narrower in frequency than most natural sources, and seemed to be somewhat periodic in nature. Whatever the cause, no one knew. Now, more than a decade later, scientists have yet to identify its mysterious source, and the pattern has never returned.

In more than fifty separate searches, only radio waves from natural phenomenon or from artificial terrestrial sources have ever been detected. Virtually all were received with already existing equipment during slow periods in their "real" research. Few scientists considered this search to be "real science," and only those whose careers and reputations were well established dared to conduct such a search. Today, all that has changed. The quest for intelligent extraterrestrial life has entered the mainstream of public consciousness, and many have taken up the quest in earnest.

THE SEARCH CONTINUES

The largest and most extensive search for extraterrestrial intelligence to date began in 1983. META (Megachannel Extraterrestrial Assay) is being operated by Harvard physicist Paul Horowitz, and is funded in part by a $100,000 grant from the Planetary Society and motion picture director Steven Spielberg.

META uses full-time the 26-meter-diameter radio telescope of Harvard and the Smithsonian Astrophysical Observatory. Together, Horowitz and his students have built most of the signal-processing equipment, and use it to listen for signals in a narrow 400,000-hertz channel around certain frequencies that seem likely carriers of alien messages. To monitor the heavens, the field of view of the stationary telescope is carried across the sky once each day by the rotating Earth. Each day the telescope is aimed at a different part of the sky and a new strip of sky is studied. After a year or so, the entire sky is surveyed, providing data from some 100 or 200 billion stars.

In the early 1990s, Horowitz began a similar project on a 26-meter telescope in Argentina, making it possible to survey the Southern Hemisphere sky with the same precision as that done in Massachusetts. So far, no intelligent extraterrestrial signals have been found from either site.

As amazing and promising as the META study has become, it is far smaller than the grand project now being conducted by the SETI (Search for Extraterrestrial Intelligence) Institute. On October 12, 1992, the symbolic five-hundredth anniversary of Columbus's discovery of the "New World," the SETI Institute, with funding from NASA, kicked off the most extensive search for intelligent radio signals from beyond ever conducted, dwarfing META in its size and capability. Sensitive receivers link with huge radio telescopes and the antennas of the spacecraft-tracking Deep Space Network located in Australia, California, Canada, and Spain to scan the entire sky for radio signals produced by intelligent life forms.

The search was designed to take a two-pronged approach. First, scientists are scrutinizing nearly 800 solar-type stars within 82 light-years of Earth, and they are studying more closely other, more promising, candidate stars for up to a day at a time. They are paying particular attention to solar-type stars within about 20 light-years of Earth, for they may have already detected television signals and may now be trying to contact *us*. SETI is able to analyze 10 million channels of spectral data per second and automatically decide if the signals are extraterrestrial or man-made.

Secondly, the project conducts a less sensitive, but more comprehensive, all-sky search. In this Microwave Observing Project (MOP), the scientists sweep their radio telescopes dozens of times across the sky, monitoring selectively 14 million separate frequency bands, each only 1 hertz wide. This decade-long search costs some $10 million per year, but will be up to ten billion times more comprehensive than all previous searches combined.

SETI actually dates back to the early 1970s, when scientists began the long and arduous task of convincing NASA—an agency whose expertise is in spacecraft—to see the benefits of a ground-based radio search for extraterrestrial intelligence. According to SETI scientist Jill Tarter, originator of the term "brown dwarf," "It's been like trying to fit a square peg into a round hole." Even more difficult was trying to convince the U.S. Congress of its necessity. "Early on [Senator William] Proxmire, in his infinite wisdom, awarded the program the Golden Fleece [in 1978]," recalls Tarter. "That one didn't hurt. It was just, 'oh yuk, yuk,' and you go on about your business.

"The real kicker was in 1981," she explains, "when the '82 budget was on the [Senate] floor. There was about seven hundred thousand dollars in the NASA budget [for SETI], and Proxmire introduced an amendment that zeroed the funding, and made it illegal for NASA to spend any of the new year's money on SETI." So for that year, the researchers illegally operated on leftover funds from the previous year's budget, and even began to write a termination plan in case funding was never restored. NASA was so infuriated that a senator would micromanage the budget down at that level that they came back with all kinds of support [the next year]," explains Tarter. "Carl Sagan and others went to talk to Proxmire, and they convinced him of some of the scientific merit of the program, and some of the social and educational secondary values of the project. He said OK, he wouldn't give us a hard time. So NASA went forward with [the project] once again."

Over the years, the SETI research and development effort had grown larger, finally becoming a full-fledged NASA project in 1990. Then, when the agency's 1991 appropriations budget went before the House, SETI again became a visible piece of its Life Sciences budget. "We were now asking for an increase from $4 million (which was the 1990 budget) to $12 million for '91 in order to actually build the hardware that we wanted to use."

On June 28, 1990, another bolt of scientific ignorance struck the program. "Out of the blue," says Tarter, "Congressman Markley, of Rhode Island, got up to introduce an amendment that said we couldn't possibly afford curiosity in this debt-ridden age, and that [the United States] just couldn't afford this project. He was seconded by Silvio Conti, who wore a pink-and-green-checkered jacket and read articles from the *National Enquirer* into the *Congressional Record*. So once again our funding was zeroed!

"This time, however, we were a little more mature and we certainly had a much larger constituency within the general public and the scientific communities. Senator [and former astronaut] Jake Garn was our big champion and, when the Senate subcommittee reported out, they reported out the full budget and even put language into the bill protecting it. The upshot is that in 1991—for the first time—we were fully funded, and facing a deadline that we'd set for ourselves: to get the instruments on the air by Columbus Day, 1992. We started out behind the curve because we didn't get our full funding the previous year, so we [had to race] like mad to make our deadline.

"But then we get down to the question of exactly what kind of signals we're looking for," explains Tarter, "because that does have something to say about the kind of hardware we build. So we just asked ourselves, 'What does nature do?' We want to look for what it *doesn't* do.

"The narrowest feature we've ever seen from an astrophysical source is three hundred hertz wide. [We decided to] look at the class of signals which are compressed in frequency below that. And then, if we find something, we've either found something pretty spectacular from nature or, perhaps, evidence of technology—an artificially generated signal." What the scientists are seeking are pulses of microwave radiation that signal the existence of an artificial technology elsewhere in the universe. "Pulses, when they're on, are very bright," explains Tarter. "When they're off, they're not transmitting any energy. So, for the same average power, you can get a much more detectable signal with a pulse. We want to be able to distinguish between artificial signals (narrowband pulses) and naturally produced pulsars (broadband pulses). So that's what we've decided to look for. And since we don't know the frequency, we want to make a systematic search through the whole microwave windows."

Of course, a signal could be hidden among billions of possible frequencies, so scientists needed to develop instruments that could look simultaneously at tens of millions of narrowband channels to have even a chance of completing the search in a reasonable time period. "We've done two things," says Tarter. "One is to say that life as we know it evolved around a solar-type star. Certainly our theorists tell us that once such stars are formed, planets are going to be the rule rather than the exception. So we've selected from available catalogs a list of [about 1,000] candidate targets which are nearby solar-type stars. We'll spend a lot of time in the targeted mode looking at those candidates with the world's largest radio telescopes to follow and track these objects for a long period of time at any frequency.

"But then we've also [recognized] that artificial signals might have a distribution of generated power. And so, by limiting our search to nearby solar-type stars that we know about, we could miss an intrinsically bright signal coming from the direction of a solar-type star that's so far away and so faint that it didn't show up in any catalog. Yet, if we were only to look in its direction, the signal itself would be bright enough that we could detect it with a more modest instrument."

The scientists are also using smaller antennas that are part of NASA's global Deep Space Network (DSN) to scan the sky rapidly at all frequencies from 1 to 10 gigahertz. Since they don't spend enough time at any one point on the sky at any frequency to allow the machine's response time to get a 1-hertz signal, they've broadened these bands to a width of 30 hertz. "With ten million at a time, we're looking at three hundred megahertz at any particular instant," says Tarter. "Now the telescope is moved at two-tenths degrees per second, which is really cranking along, so it will be something like six or seven years until we've completed a sky survey of all directions at these frequencies. We may find an intrinsically strong signal that we would miss if we just limited it to nearby targets, so we're putting our eggs in at least two baskets, because we know so little."

Being part of one of the grandest searches in history has Tarter very excited. "There's an easy way to phrase it," she explains. "When I was a postdoc at Ames and [studying] brown dwarfs, I was having a great time. It was a lot of fun. It was intellectually challenging and interesting and I was learning new things and, maybe, understanding the universe a little better. But the man on the street was paying my salary, and I sort of always wondered—I'm having a great time, but what's he getting out of it? But then, when I started to work on SETI, [I realized] that I'm doing something which might, in fact, have a profound influence on the [person] on the street that's paying my salary.

"I feel really good about it but, sometimes, I have a hard time explaining that my real interest is the detection of a signal. And that's enough. If I get the signal, that's just so incredible, that I really don't spend a whole lot of time thinking about what will it say. The simple answering of that very fundamental question is a big enough goal for me. And I very well realize that the chance of my answering it is very small. I mean, this is an enormous search and, although what we're doing is hundreds of millions or billions of times more comprehensive than what we've done in the last thirty years, there's no way that I can predict success. But I sure can promise *no* success if we don't try."

Since the SETI project began in 1992, NASA cut the project once again from its budget—this time for good, and sent researchers scurrying for private funding to continue the work. Despite its repeated setbacks, the project has become operational and has become the first comprehensive search for extraterrestrial intelligence in history.

SEARCHING FOR GAIA

Searching for intelligent radio messages from across the far reaches of the galaxy is indeed a mind-boggling concept but, by limiting the search to *intelligent* life, scientists may be limiting the chances of success in answering the question: Are we alone in the universe? What about the potentially thousands or millions of planets on which may have arisen life that has not yet evolved to intelligence? How can we ever hope to find this life without digging in the soil of its parent world? Despite its seeming impossibility, such a prospect may actually be possible by applying what has recently been learned about the atmospheric balance of the Earth to those planets that may exist among the stars.

Suppose astronomers should one day see the light of a planet in orbit around a nearby star. Even the best photos taken from the largest orbiting superscopes (such as Roger Angel's proposed 16-meter behemoth) would provide little more than a speck of light to study, yet spectroscopic analysis of that light would reveal the chemical and physical properties of the world's atmosphere. If that world's spectrum should show a predominantly nitrogen- and oxygen-rich atmosphere like that of Earth, one could be fairly certain that this atmospheric composition would not occur without some help. For one thing, both nitrogen and oxygen are unstable as free molecules and would attach themselves to other chemicals rather quickly if left alone. Of course, the planet could be caught at just the time before the chemicals have been transformed, but the probability of that is extremely unlikely. More probable is that there would be something on the world that is continually resupplying the atmosphere with its nitrogen and oxygen. Based on what scientists know about the Earth's biosphere, one possibility would be life. Another, of course, would be some previously unknown chemistry like that which showed up on Mars in 1976.

Suppose significant quantities of methane gas were found as well. On Earth, methane is produced mainly by bacteria that live in swampy marshes, and in the forward stomachs of grass-eating animals. Methane and oxygen cannot coexist in the presence of ultraviolet radiation, a commodity plentiful in the vicinity of stars; therefore, if they should be found together in the atmosphere of an alien world, it would strongly suggest that each must continually be regenerated and resupplied to the atmosphere at least as fast as they are reacting. The only source known that could possibly generate both gases together is life.

So it is entirely possible that the presence of extraterrestrial life can be detected by searching for evidence of unusually great organic activity in the atmospheres of distant extrasolar planets. Still, first the planets, themselves, must be found.

EPILOGUE

As it has been true for centuries, indeed, for millennia, everyone seems excited about the possibility of finding planetary systems around distant stars and, especially, about locating Earth-like planets having the potential for sustaining intelligent life. Many people, scientists or not, believe that other planets are commonplace—that they form as a natural by-product of the birth of stars—but this belief is not unanimous, and has certainly not been proved.

Despite years of discovery followed by disappointment, astronomers are now even more encouraged and they are armed with ever more powerful telescopic instrumentation and observational strategies. An all-out race to find planets in orbit around other stars is now underway. Yet, despite their efforts, astronomers could never prove convincingly the existence of a single planet in orbit around another star. Until 1992, that is.

While working with a powerful radio telescope at the Arecibo Observatory in Puerto Rico, Pennsylvania State University astronomers Drs. Alex Wolszczan and Dale Frail detected something most unusual coming from the pulsar B1257+12, about 1600 light-years distant in the constellation of Virgo.

PULSAR PLANETS

Pulsars are remnants of supernova explosions—the death of massive stars that blast their atmospheres into space and leave behind a hot dense core—a neutron star. With barely the diameter of a large city, these stellar corpses rotate extremely rapidly—often hundreds of times per second—and send beams of high-energy radiation outward like beacons from a lighthouse. As the beams sweep past our line of sight here on Earth, astronomers detect them as pulses of light: hence the name "pulsars." Since pulsars radiate with periods that can be timed to within an accuracy of millionths of a second, even the slightest outside effect on their motions can be measured precisely. And that's exactly what Wolszczan and Frail found: sometimes the pulses from B1257+12 arrived a millisecond earlier or later than one would expect from a single, isolated pulsar.

The discoverers argued that these subtle, yet repetitive, Doppler variations in the time of arrival of the pulsar beam were caused by an orbiting planet tugging on the pulsar—away from Earth, then toward Earth. This unexpected result was met with some skepticism but, after continuing with more accurate timing observations, Wolszczan's team concluded in 1994 that the object's observed variations could only be explained by the existence of three planets in orbits much closer to the pulsar than Earth is to our Sun. Two of these each have approximately 3 Earth masses and lie in orbits of one-third and one-half the size of Earth's orbit around the Sun. The third "planet" has a mass (0.015 Earth's) similar to our Moon and revolves in an orbit five times closer than Earth's. This inferred system of planetary companions was confirmed when Wolszczan's data also revealed mutual gravitational interactions among the three individual planets as required by the theory of gravity. In fact, a fourth object is also suspected in a much wider orbit with a revolution period exceeding the five-year duration of present studies.

What makes this discovery so bizarre is that the planets orbit the remnant of a supernova explosion—a star that may have originally existed as part of a binary system. After the supernova of one star, the companion star evaporated and spilled some of its material onto the pulsar, helping to spin it to its current rotational rate of 160 times per second. Few scientists believe that planets can survive the explosion of their parent star. So where did these planets come from in this turbulent and hostile environment? If they existed in the original binary system (something astronomers don't yet understand), would they have survived the supernova explosion? If they coalesced from debris blown off from the blast (again, a process not well understood), wouldn't the vaporization of the stellar companion interfere with their birth? At present, no one knows for sure, and the debate continues as this manuscript goes to press.

WHERE HAVE ALL THE JUPITERS GONE?

Although these "pulsar-planets" may not be the life-sustaining worlds we'd like to find, their existence around a pulsar seems to indicate that the process of planetary formation is robust and can occur even in hostile situations. The discovery encourages scientists to look even harder around more normal stars. Unfortunately, planets around normal stars are proving elusive. In fact, the radial velocity searches of nearly 100 nearby stars did not reveal any Jupiter-mass planets or the more massive brown dwarfs, even though the technology was capable of detecting them.

The idea that Jupiter-like planets might be rare gained strong support from other studies, too. First, Dr. Ben Zuckerman and colleagues observed that the circumstellar environments of young stars become rapidly depleted of orbiting gas needed to build such planets. His research indicates that stars blow away their supply of gaseous raw material between one and ten million years after their birth; thus, any Jupiter-mass planets would need to form within that time. Second, even in our own solar system astronomers have had great difficulty in developing theoretical models of Jupiter's formation.

Planetary systems consisting exclusively of terrestrial, rocky planets could certainly exist without the accompanying Jovian planets which clearly dominate our own solar system. However, there would be significant consequences for possible life-forms. As pointed out by Dr. George Wetherill, the inner terrestrial planets would no longer be shielded from catastrophic impacts of cometary objects, subjecting the evolution of life-forms on the inner planets to occasional mass extinctions. In our solar system, the strong gravitational pulls of Jupiter and Saturn deflect such impactors away from the Earth and inner planets. This shielding effect was dramatically illustrated by the violent impact events associated with comet Shoemaker-Levy 9 on Jupiter in July 1994.

ADVANCES IN INDIRECT DETECTION

If Jupiter-mass planets are rare, then perhaps the lack of success in finding them simply means that astronomers need to search many more stars. One way of accomplishing this involves detecting subtle brightness changes in the parent star caused by gravitational micro-lensing from another star or by eclipses caused by a star's own planets.

The first idea is based on the fact that light bends when traversing a gravitational field. If, for example, we are fortuitously monitoring the brightness of a distant star when a much fainter, closer star happens to move directly along our line of sight, the first star's brightness could increase as its light, already journeying to us, is bent and magnified by the gravitational influence of the intervening star. This effect is called gravitational lensing. It can occur because stars in our galaxy are all in orbit around the galactic center with revolution periods dependent on their distance from the center. Although these periods are measured in millions or hundreds of millions of years, there are billions of stars in our galaxy so there is a finite probability of a few such chance alignments occurring in our lifetimes.

Such lensing events have already been observed. Astronomers can monitor the brightnesses of millions of stars on a daily basis using wide-field electronic cameras and fast computers. A typical lensing event produced by chance alignments of stars can last about one month. However, if the closer star also has an orbiting planetary system, the individual planets can also act as lenses, producing an additional hour-long increase in brightness of the more distant star. To detect such an event would require hourly monitoring of stars undergoing brightening activity. By operating a worldwide around-the-clock monitoring program, astronomers have proposed to accomplish this task which would lead to the detection of Earth-like planets.

Gravitational micro-lensing offers the opportunity to accumulate statistics on the prevalence of planets around other stars. However, each event is a once-in-a-lifetime occurrence and does not lend itself to follow-up observations because that particular alignment will never occur again.

Similarly, astronomers can also search for changes in a star's brightness when a chance alignment enables its own planets to partially eclipse the star itself. Viewed from a distance and in a favorable orientation, our own Jupiter's transit across the Sun would cause a 1% diminution of the Sun's brightness over a 30-hour period. In contrast to gravitational micro-lensing, however, eclipses would occur repetitively (approximately 12 years for Jupiter), helping to confirm an initial "discovery." A space-based mission has been proposed to search for eclipses from Earth-like planets. The FRESIP (FRequency of Earth-Sized Inner Planets) instrument would regularly monitor the brightnesses of 5,000 solar-type stars for a period of eight years.

ADVANCES IN DIRECT DETECTION

Using sophisticated adaptive optics and laser guide stars to correct for atmospheric blurring, it now appears possible to directly

detect Jupiter- or Saturn-like planets from six- to ten-meter diameter telescopes on the Earth rather than solely from space-based
instruments. Dr. Roger Angel of the University of Arizona and
Dr. David Sandler of Thermo Trex Corp. have recently proposed
such methods to detect Jupiter-like bodies in orbit around solar-
type stars after using only a few hours of observation.

Space-based interferometers have also been proposed to image
planetary systems in the infrared where thermal emission from
warm planets is highest. From above Earth's blurring and
infrared-bright atmosphere, such instruments can strongly atten-
uate the direct light from the parent star while passing the light
from any off-center, orbiting planets. Once planets have been
detected, their infrared spectra can be examined to search for
indirect evidence of photosynthetic life. For example, such spectra might reveal oxygen, methane, and water vapor in a planet's
atmosphere.

Both NASA and the European Space Agency are considering
such space missions. The European project is known as DAR-
WIN. The proposed U.S. instrument is OASES, Outpost for
the Analysis and Spectroscopy of Exo-Solar Systems. To work
at maximum efficiency, both these interferometers must be
launched to distances beyond Jupiter to avoid looking through
the warm zodiacal dust which orbits the Sun near the terrestrial
planets.

1995: A YEAR TO BE REMEMBERED

The NASA ''Roadmap'' Study

The current search for extrasolar planets is fueled by ever more
impressive technologies and is intensifying at a rapid rate. In
early 1995, NASA officials funded a new level of activity by
announcing an opportunity for scientific groups to propose
search strategies, which could influence official NASA policy in
the years and decades ahead! Astronomers were challenged to

propose "Roadmaps": a series of investigations, missions, and milestones leading ultimately to detailed imaging of Earth-like planets around other stars. These strategies would be part of a year-long study process which would merge into a single Roadmap plan to be considered by the NASA Administrator, Dan Goldin, as part of NASA's long-term strategic plan.

Roadmap plans were developed by three primary teams centered at the University of Arizona, the Smithsonian Center for Astrophysics, and the Jet Propulsion Lab. Each team melded together a diverse group of individuals: astronomers (foreign and U.S.), physicists, engineers, aerospace administrators, and other scientists. In total, over 100 experts participated directly with input from a broader world community. As this book goes to press, the three separate Roadmaps have been merged into a single plan by a Blue Ribbon Panel, chaired by Nobel laureate Dr. Charles Townes. The NASA Administrator will shortly begin considering the proposed recommendations, but already it seems clear that NASA will heartily endorse the search and characterization of extrasolar Earth-like planets as a major initiative. Indeed, in the summer of 1995, NASA established a separate office for such research, ExNPS (Exploration of Neighboring Planetary Systems).

As the NASA Roadmap studies proceded, two revolutionary discoveries were announced at an October 1995 meeting in Florence, Italy, ironically near the resting place of Galileo Galilei. Two new milestones now appear to have been achieved: the discoveries of a planetary object around a solar-type star and also of a bona-fide brown dwarf.

A REAL EXTRASOLAR PLANET
AROUND 51 PEG

Using the indirect search technique of radial velocity variations, astronomers Michael Mayor and Didier Queloz of Geneva Observatory have apparently detected a planet roughly half the mass of Jupiter orbiting a star similar to our Sun known as 51 Pegasus, which lies 42 light-years from us.

Unexpectedly, the new planet orbits its sun very rapidly, in 4.2 days, in an orbit five times closer than that of Mercury! As a result, the star's variation in radial velocity is large, nearly 100 meters/sec, and is easy to detect in only a few nights of observation. In fact, the initial discovery was quickly confirmed by two separate teams of U.S. astronomers. The proximity of this planet to its sun is so surprising that astronomers have considered alternate interpretations of the data such as the effects of rapidly rotating star spots and the possibility of a highly inclined orbit for a much more massive orbiting companion. At present, however, these explanations appear to be highly unlikely.

Many questions are being asked about this new mystery world. Surprisingly, it appears that a Jupiter-like planet could actually survive in such a hot (approximately 1800 C) environment. According to theoretical astrophysicist, Dr. Adam Burrows, the planet's own gravity could retain an initial gaseous atmosphere, although a gas giant planet would certainly swell to a larger size. How this planet formed is a real mystery! Could it possibly have originated in its present orbit, in which case could it form before the star blew away the raw material? Perhaps the planet originated elsewhere and was perturbed into its present orbit. If so, there must be other planetary objects orbiting 51 Peg.

Ironically, this new planet could have been discovered *much* earlier. Its detection did not require highly sophisticated new technology, but it did require looking in the right place with the right timing. Astronomers simply did not expect to find such large planets in such small orbits and had limited their searches to looking for planetary systems resembling our own.

A REAL BROWN DWARF: GLIESE 229B

At the same conference in Florence, discovery of the first brown dwarf was announced by astronomers from Caltech and Johns Hopkins University. Using a technique for removing atmospheric blurring, a group led by Drs. Tadashi Nakajima and Shrinivas Kulkarni used direct detection to "see" a cool companion around the red dwarf star, Gliese 229, located some 30 light-years away from us in the constellation Lepus.

Although brown dwarf discoveries have been claimed many times before, Gl 229B has the distinction of being the coolest, lowest luminosity candidate. Perhaps most conclusive, however, is its spectrum, which shows the obvious presence of atmospheric methane, reminiscent of Jupiter's spectrum. The spectrum so clearly indicates a brown dwarf that a mass measurement may not be needed to confirm its status. Based on comparisons with theoretical models, the mass is estimated to be about twenty times Jupiter's mass.

Is Gl 229B a planet? Afterall it is a nonstellar object in orbit around a star. Unfortunately, we do not know whether it formed from an accumulating disk of material around its sun, as we believe our planetary system formed, or from a completely separate blob of gravitating material in the way we presume binary star companions form. Perhaps there are other objects in the Gl 229 system which will help us answer this question.

As with 51 Peg's planet, the brown dwarf could have been discovered *much* earlier. Other astronomers have imaged Gl 229 with enough sensitivity to detect the companion. However, previous searches concentrated either too close-in or too far away from the central star to be successful. Again it was necessary to look in the right place with the right technique.

TO BOLDLY GO . . .

These new discoveries coming on the heels of the pulsar planets clearly indicate that planetary formation can occur in unusual situations. "Unusual" in the sense that they are different from objects in our own solar system. Or is it *we* who are unusual? Until systems of planetary objects are charted and characterized, we will not know. However, the next decade, with its new technologies, should enable us to answer this question.

Expenditures of time and resources in this research don't seem totally ridiculous when one considers the impact of finding another planetary system with Earth-mass planets around a solar-type star. We may even get detailed photographs of other Earth-like planets, showing indications of climates favorable to other life-forms. History has shown that the first photos of the whole Earth from space revolutionized our views not only of the planet itself, but also of ourselves. Imagine the revolution in human thought that would begin with such a picture of another Earth!

Perhaps even more staggering than the scientific benefits of these discoveries are the philosophical implications. "A lot of the population, including many scientists, believe that our solar system is unique, that something peculiar happened here to form planets," says Bradford Smith, now of the University of Hawaii. "These discoveries show that if there is only one more solar system out there, there surely must be others."

If astronomers are correct, then a glance at the nighttime sky may encompass not only thousands of stars, but possibly thousands of planets and even—who knows—countless civilizations like our own. Only time will tell if the ancient vision of Epicurus was correct.

Another discovery could come any day now.

INDEX